Other Heroes
of the
Book of Mormon

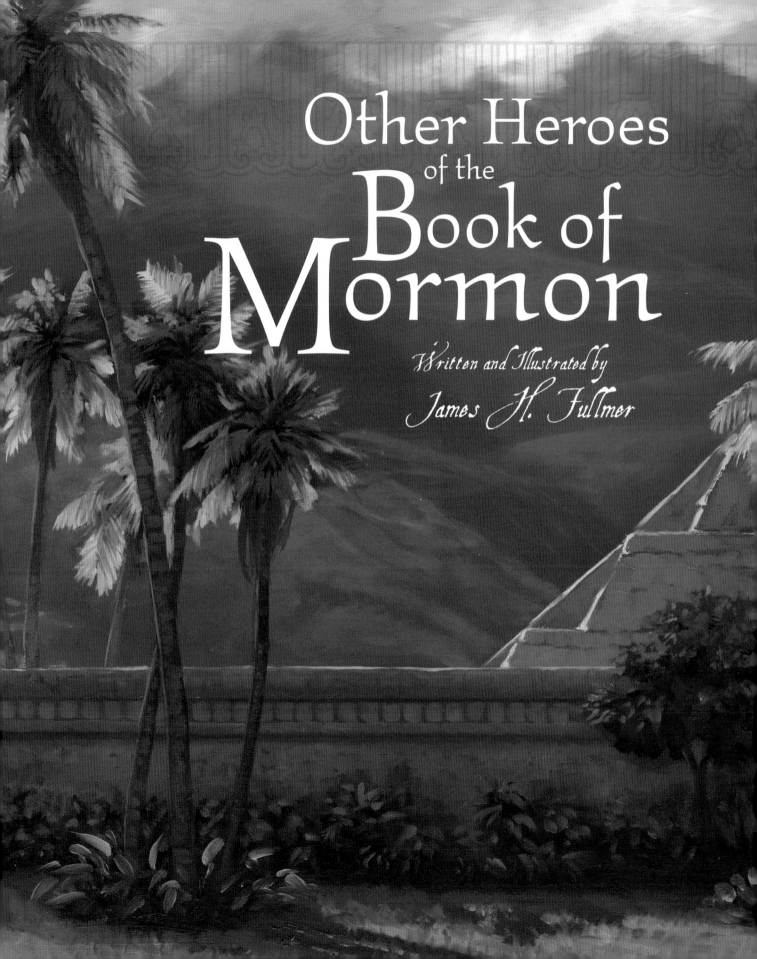

Other Heroes
of the
Book of
Mormon

Written and Illustrated by

James H. Fullmer

Dedicated to all my mentors and teachers who
helped me see deeper into the scriptures than I
ever could have on my own.

❖

Acknowledgments

This book would not exist without two people: Al Waller believed in this project and gave me the support I needed to work on it full time for many months. This would also have been a very different book (and a much less interesting one) if not for Noelle Perner, an indispensable editor and guide, who led me during the development of the manuscript. She helped me sculpt the words to tell the stories that mean so much to me.

I also thank my wife, who worked double duty for two years while I put my ideas on paper. I thank my test readers, particularly Joe Kindt, who shares my passion for these stories. He gave me feedback and challenged my interpretation of the Book of Mormon text, which was helpful beyond measure. My brother Rob also helped me understand the geography of Book of Mormon lands and introduced me to many great references. When I needed encouragement, he reassured me that I could do this and that my idea wasn't a disaster. Norb and Heidi Schmidt, David Maruska, and Lynda Kasper deserve heartfelt thanks for providing the means to finally get the artwork done for this book.

My final thanks goes to all those in the past who risked their lives and sacrificed their resources so that we could have this incredible record—the Book of Mormon.

Published by Covenant Communications, Inc.
American Fork, Utah

Copyright © 2011 by James H. Fullmer

Printed in China
First Printing: September 2011

17 16 15 14 13 12 11   10 9 8 7 6 5 4 3 2 1

ISBN 978-1-60861-462-2

Table of Contents –

Lands of the Book of Mormon

by
James H. Fullmer
based on the scholarship of
John L. Sorenson in,
"Mormon's Map"

● - Settlement (town, village, city)
★ - Capital city
▲ - Mountain or Hill
ABC - Land

MORON

Ablom ●

hill Cumorah ▲

Shem ●
Jordan ●   ▲ hill Shin

ANTUM

DESOLATION

Boaz ●
Desolation ●   Teancum ●

narrow pass

Bountiful ●
Mulek ●
Gid ●
Jershon ●   Omner ●   Morianton ●
Moroni ●

BOUNTIFUL   Lehi ●

Nephihah ●
hill Onidah ▲

ANTIONUM

Aaron ●   SIRON

Ammonihah ●

Noah ●

river Sidon

ZARAHEMLA

Melek ●

Wilderness of
Hermounts

★ hill Amnihu
Zarahemla

Gideon ●

river Sidon

Judea ●
MINON

Cumeni ●
Zeezrom ●   Manti ●   ▲ hill Riplah
Antiparah ●

valley of Alma

Helam ●

AMULON

Jerusalem ●   waters of Mormon
Mormon ●

ISHMAEL   NEPHI

Ani-Anti ●

MIDDONI

Shilom ●   ★ Nephi   ▲ mount Antipas

SHEMLON

FIRST INHERITANCE

Author's Note

These pages will take you on a wonderful journey through the Book of Mormon—but it will not be the one you are used to. This is the record of ancient America as told from the perspective of the *hidden* stories. When it comes to the scriptures, I look for the facts, but as I read I create a story in my mind—a movie of sorts. After pondering on how best to tell these stories and exploring many different options, I decided that sharing my "movies," based on the facts I could determine, would be the way to go. You are now holding the fruits of those labors in your hands.

My journey into the world of scripture was a slow one from the start. I was not a good reader when I was young. Reading was hard for me, and although I loved hearing the stories found in those sacred pages (my dad was a great storyteller, and my mother was an expressive reader), my love of the scriptures didn't come until later.

It was on my mission that I first built a personal relationship with prophets like Moses, Peter, Nephi, and Alma. My understanding of the mission of the Savior grew, and my love of Christ increased as I became invested in the lives of His servants. In the scriptures I found great examples of how I could live my life to come closer to Christ.

During my years of teaching seminary, I came to appreciate many of the stories that are not well known. In these "smaller" stories, I found people I could really relate to, like Aminadab, Ammon (descendant of Zarahemla), and the maidservant of Morianton. They were not perfect, but the Lord still had a great work for them to do.

Feel free to simply enjoy the stories, but if these narratives pique your curiosity, you'll find notes at the end of each chapter. There I reference scriptures and discuss why I made the creative decisions I did. I hope that you'll find them to be an additional enrichment of the scriptural account. My deepest hope is that these stories will excite and inspire you to take a closer look at the Book of Mormon.

PEOPLE, PLACES, AND THINGS

Many people enjoy reading scriptures just fine without worrying about where events took place, what people looked like, and what their lives were like. As an artist and storyteller, I cannot. For me to depict these events, I had to lock down answers to these very questions. My choices regarding the location, race, and overall look of the Book of Mormon world came

from reading a lot of what has been published by a variety of LDS scholars over the years, but I ultimately accept responsibility for my creative decisions. My vision of race in the Book of Mormon is very diverse. While I do wish for every cultural group to be able to see themselves in these stories, my decisions were also based on archaeological evidence. Faces with Asian, African, and even middle-eastern characteristics are found in ancient Mesoamerican art. I tried to represent that.

THE MAP

Many different maps have been created to illustrate possible Book of Mormon lands, and there is much discussion and debate about them. I feel the most compelling arguments are those made for a Mesoamerican setting, which is what I used for my descriptions. I did not, however, wish to create a map corresponding with specific modern locations, as these are continuously being studied and debated. I wanted a map representing what the Book of Mormon says about its own geography. No work using this approach has impressed me more than John L. Sorenson's "Mormon's Map." My map is based on his scholarship, and it is not meant to represent any existing locations.

NOTE ABOUT TIMELINES

Coming up with a definitive timeline is quite challenging due to vacancies in the information we have, both in the text and in the historical landscape. There is a reason why the Church's scripture committee included the word *about* before all dates in the newest (online version) edition of the scriptures. It was important to me, however, to include some kind of timeline to help the reader see where these stories fit into the overall Book of Mormon history. I have done my best to make, what I consider, informed estimates on many of the dates that we just don't know, but all the dates should only be considered a guide to the placement of events in our stories.

Before you is the culmination of years of work and uncountable hours of study, painting, writing, and praying. I hope my efforts offer you a new and exciting view of one of the most important testimonies of Christ.

Jaredites
The First Inhabitants of the Promised Land

According to the records we currently have, the earliest group to inherit the promised land of the Americas was the people of Jared. An abbreviated account of this civilization is included in the Book of Mormon and is known as the book of Ether. The account follows Jared and his righteous brother, who, through the Lord's guidance, brought their people to the promised land from the Tower of Babel, possibly as early as 3000 BC (Genesis 11:1–9; Ether 1:33). They settled in the land north of the narrow neck (Alma 22:30), where they flourished and eventually covered the land. By the time the people of Lehi and Mulek arrived around 600 BC, the Jaredite civilization was collapsing toward a complete destruction as the people annihilated themselves in a civil war.

*I*n an era of intrigue and lust for power, one loyal band of brothers would stop at nothing to protect the rightful king.

1 Sons of Shule
Faithful and True

➤ *Ether 7* ❧

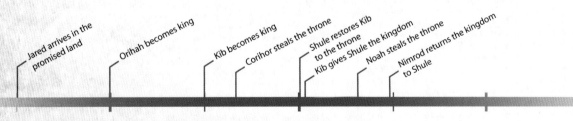

Jared arrives in the promised land

Orihah becomes king

Kib becomes king

Corihor steals the throne

Shule restores Kib to the throne

Kib gives Shule the kingdom

Noah steals the throne

Nimrod returns the kingdom to Shule

Dates are not available

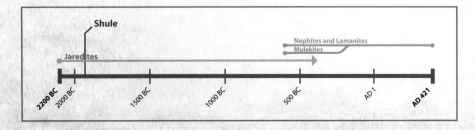

Shule

Nephites and Lamanites
Mulekites

Jaredites

2200 BC 2000 BC   1500 BC   1000 BC   500 BC   AD 1   AD 421

The queen's arm was wrapped gently in his as king Shule strolled toward his peaceful garden courtyard. He had spent the morning holding court and ministering to the needs of his people, but Shule loved to work with his hands, and any opportunity to labor in his garden was time well treasured.

The sun was shining, and Shule breathed deep the sweet smell of leaves and soil as he entered the courtyard. He was just unbuckling the belt of his sword to set it aside when he sensed it. The courtyard was too quiet. All the sounds of the birds were muted for they, like the king, had the unmistakable impression that predators were on the hunt. Suddenly, footsteps exploded through the grass from the columns behind him. In one fluid movement, Shule stepped in front of his queen, spun around to face his attackers, and held his unsheathed sword aloft like a staff as he advanced on his enemy. The youthful assailants, sticks like swords raised high above their heads, were so surprised by this response that they had no time to stop their forward momentum or swerve to avoid the now imminent collision. It was over in an instant.

Standing now, the king surveyed the faces of three of his sons, who were now sprawled on the ground around him. He shook his head in mock disappointment.

"Sloppy," he said simply. "I heard you stalking us all the way through the palace."

Shule turned his back on them and walked back toward his wife, whose arms were outstretch to receive him. Both of them tried desperately to conceal a smile.

"It's not possible that you heard us!" said the oldest, Mulok, sounding incredulous as he arose and helped his brothers to their feet. In truth, the king had heard nothing. His sons were becoming very good at this game.

Shule paused as he reached his wife. "So you think you can take me this time?" he challenged his sons. "Three on one?"

"Child's play" shot back Shiloh, the youngest and smallest of the three. His size, however, belied a fierce warrior, who, like his brothers, Shule knew not to underestimate. It had become increasingly difficult to outmaneuver his sons in their sparring games. They were learning to collaborate in clever and strategic ways, and the king knew that the days when he could take all three of them were quickly coming to a close.

He smiled when he saw each of them crouched in tense defensive poses, looking expectantly at him.

Shule faced his wife and handed her his sword. The steel gleamed in the sunlight, and for a brief moment, Shule remembered the day he had forged it. The Hill Ephraim had rung with the sound of iron against steel while he hammered the billet[1] that would soon become a shining blade, a sword that, along with its brothers, would return his father, Kib, to the throne that was rightfully his. Kib had been in captivity since before Shule was born. Corihor, Kib's oldest son,[2] had rebelled and formed an army in the land of Nehor to usurp the throne. He'd been victorious, and from that day on a dark shadow had settled over the land. But now, that shadow was gone. Peace had been hard won, but Shule basked in its warm embrace.

"I fear we shall die of old age before our venerable father can be troubled to join his challengers." Ezra's taunt, dripping with sarcasm, brought an abrupt end to Shule's reveries. He kissed his

wife, leaving the sword in her care and pulling a stake from the garden as he advanced toward his sons. In a moment, there was a flurry of movement, and the battle had begun.

"Brothers, see here," called out Ezra as he parried a playful attack from his father. "Before you is the mighty king Shule who rescued his father from captivity."

"But that was so long ago," continued Mulok with a wink, "and he was much younger then."

"Songs are still sung of that day," the queen said, sitting on the grass and enjoying the games before her. "The mighty and faithful Shule had brought down his wicked brother, Corihor, and restored the throne to the rightful king."

"Corihor is our uncle," Shiloh said devotedly as he dodged a halfhearted strike from his father. "He is a good man and loyal to us. Whatever his past, I would not call him 'wicked.'"

"Of course, you are right," the queen consented. "Corihor has proven his allegiance to the rightful king. All has long since been forgiven. His son Noah, on the other hand . . ." the queen trailed off darkly.

Shule brought his stick down hard against Shiloh's, knocking it to the ground. Shiloh looked up in surprise. Shule glanced at his wife and winked. Turning back to his sons, he raised his arms to indicate they could attack at will. "I have heard the rumors," the king answered, moving to dodge two attacks at once, "but I do not think there is any merit in them." Again, Shule moved and found an opening, delivering a good-natured but stinging blow to Shiloh's flank. His son stepped back, nursing his wound and leaving his brothers to try to take down their father. "He is restless, and I believe he has inherited the same lust for power that his father had but—" Shule paused momentarily as Mulok rushed in to test an opening. Shule quickly dispatched the boy with a strike to his sword hand, inflicting just enough pain that his son dropped his stick to rub his sore knuckles. "But," Shule continued, eyeing Ezra, who was the last one standing, "who would follow him if he rebelled? My kingdom has spread across the face of the land, and my people are happy."

The other two sons rejoined their brother, this time surrounding their father on all sides. Shule eyed the conspirators. "Except for this uprising, of course." His expression changed to mock despair. "And among my own sons too. Which of you would like the crown?" he asked teasingly.

None of his sons answered. They were looking back and forth at each other, communicating in a secret language all their own, a language known only to brothers. Shule crouched a little, ready for the slightest provocation. "Who among you is strong enough to bear the weight of my crown?" Shule taunted.

The queen looked on, quietly curious of the outcome. She couldn't conceal her pride for the skilled young warriors her sons were becoming. None of the sons responded for a moment, but then Ezra replied, "I will take your crown, Father."

"Take it, then. I give it freely." With incredible speed, King Shule spun and cracked Ezra on the crown of his head before the young man even had a chance to respond. Immediately, Shule felt a sharp sting on his flank and another across his back. Turning to face his clever aggressors, he got another hit from behind as Ezra rejoined the fight, rubbing the top of his head. No matter which way Shule turned, he was exposed to the blows of one of his warrior sons. There was nothing left to do but submit. He knelt and discarded his stick, pleading for mercy. But his sons showed none as they piled onto their father amidst laughter and shouts of "Death to the king! Death to the king!"

When Shule had finally thrown his sons off of him and sat beside his queen once more, he attempted to smooth his clothes. "I disown all of you. The only thing you will inherit is the sole of my shoe," Shule declared, a little out of breath.

The queen nudged Shule genially, and they shared an impish smile.

The sons, meanwhile, ignored their father's decree as they turned the battle on each other and wrestled in the grass.

The king put his arm around his wife and kissed her forehead. The two of them watched their sons for a moment, celebrating the joy of the family God had given them.

"I know Noah might be dangerous," Shule whispered to his wife. "Although he may hold sway over his brothers, I cannot imagine he could ever draw away enough of the people to stage an uprising." Shule smiled comfortingly at his wife, who placed her head on his shoulder. Secretly, however, Shule's heart did not hold the same confidence as his words. The rumors had become more numerous, and he knew there was more truth to them than he was letting on.

In the days that followed, the whispers of an insurgence continued to grow until, on one fateful morning, a shout came from just outside the palace, and a mighty roar of voices answered it. Shule and his family were working in the garden again when the turmoil broke loose. The sound of rushing wind followed the warning, and Shule's eyes widened. He knew the sound well. "Arrows!" he shouted, quickly waving his sons away. "Find shelter! Run!" He could say nothing more before a shower of deadly shafts rained down on the garden.

Shule's sons sprinted to the shelter of a colonnade, while Shule only had time to shield his wife with his own body. A single arrow had struck him near his shoulder, and he grimaced at the pain. He looked around in horror at the bodies now strewn about the courtyard. For many of the servants and courtiers, the warning had come too late. His wife shuddered underneath him. Shule looked down to see that, although he had blocked one, two other arrows had found the queen. He cried out in agony as his beloved wife drew her last breath and then lay lifeless beneath him. For a moment, Shule could not move, but then he looked toward his sons and, in a calm, clear voice, said, "Escape, now."

"Where should we go?" Mulok asked soberly, fighting down the anguish rising inside him.

"Your uncle's palace in Nehor. Go quickly, and do not be seen."

Shule's sons obeyed their father's command and fled into the palace. Shule spared only a moment to watch them go. His eyes filled with tears as he looked down at his wife's still body. Her soul had left her.[3]

The sound of invading footsteps echoed across the hallways and courtyards of the palace. Shule slowly stood and drew his sword, anger mounting as he thought of his loss, and moved toward the sound of battle.

In the council chamber of Nehor, Corihor listened to the report of his informants with a grave countenance. The debriefing ended just as Shule's sons rushed into the room.

"What news of the war, Uncle?" Mulok asked, hungry for any information.

Corihor dismissed his advisors and motioned for his nephews to sit with him. "The land of Moron is lost. Noah and his brothers have taken the capital and pushed on to capture more lands. It was in this last campaign that Noah succeeded in capturing the king, your father."

Mulok cursed Noah's name.

When Corihor was thirty-two, he left Moron and dwelt in Nehor where he drew away many people. When he gathered an army he invaded Moron and took his father, Kib, captive.

Ablom●

Nehor●

▲
Hill Riplah

Moron●

When Kib was very old, he begat Shule, who armed his people and invaded Nehor to restore his father to the throne.

narrow pass

Shiloh asked cautiously, "Our father will be all right? Is it not the tradition among our people to spare the life of a captured king?"

Corihor looked at his nephew and searched for the right words to cushion his answer.

"Surely you spared your father," Shiloh continued, uncomfortable with Corihor's silence. "And my father spared you . . ."

"Noah sees a destructive pattern in this," Corihor began soberly. "Yes, I spared my father when I rebelled against him, and because I did, your father was born. He was the only brother of mine courageous enough to challenge me. Because of him, I lost my kingdom. I should have lost my life." Corihor paused and gazed pointedly at each of the young men before him. "But your father showed me mercy, and I have been loyal to him ever since. My sons, however . . ."

Corihor stood and walked to one of the many windows in the room, visibly wrestling with his feelings concerning his sons' betrayal. "Noah, in particular, could think of nothing but the loss of his inheritance. Your father spared my life, and in return my sons rose up in rebellion and seized his throne. It seems to be the consequence of mercy."

Ezra slowly rose to his feet as though carrying a heavy burden. "What is going to happen to our father?"

"Noah wants to ensure that no sons can rise up to take his throne. He intends . . . to put Shule to death."

Now all the brothers were on their feet. "When?"

"I don't know," Corihor lamented, the age showing on his lined face. "Soon."

Mulok looked at his brothers. They nodded, knowing now what they must do.

Quiet as shadows in the dead of night, Shule's sons moved easily across the darkened courtyard of their former home.[4] The royal palace in Moron seemed oddly foreign to them. Though it had only been a matter of days since their family had resided within the supposed safety of its walls, it was different now. Someone else lived there. It would not feel like home again until that enemy had been driven out.

It was vitally important that each part of their plan be perfectly executed. They would not get a second chance to rescue their father. If they did not succeed, he would be executed the next day.

They entered the palace through the servants' quarters and found many of the same servants still there. They knew they had to tread carefully in case of shifted allegiances, but they also knew which servants had never faltered during their father's reign. They left the quarters armed with all the information they needed on the location of the guards and where Noah was keeping their father, but even though they longed to find their father, the prison was not their first stop.

King Noah awoke from his slumber, his heart thudding in his chest. He thought he'd heard something, but when he scanned the dark room, everything seemed normal. He slowed his breathing, trying to calm his beating heart, yet he could sense something was not right. Noah looked again, straining his eyes against the blackness. This time his sight rested on a shadow near the window. Something was crouching there. Paralyzed by uncertainly and fear, he remained where he was. He could hear his own panicked breathing and was unnerved by how loud it sounded in the deathly quiet of the night. The shadow did not move, and he began to wonder if he had imagined the whole thing. Then he thought he saw a slight movement. His eyes widened as the shadows moved toward him like wraiths, filling his vision. Before he could scream, the shadows brought their weapons down hard and fast in the moonlight, silencing Noah forever.

Shule's sons stealthily made their way out of the royal house and crept along the shadows near the prison entrance. Without a sound, they slew the unsuspecting guards and broke down the prison doors. There stood their father. Shule gathered them in his arms for one brief moment and simply said, "I knew you would come."

Together they fled into the night.

"Our father returned with us to our people, and you know the rest of the story," Shiloh said, reveling in the retelling of the story. He never tired of entertaining his young audience.

"No, I don't," replied Omer incredulously. The boy was embroiled in a battle with his much older brothers, dodging blows and attacking with his stick sword.

Many years had passed since that night. Shule and his second wife sat in the shade of the palace courtyard, watching the display. Considering all the warfare he had seen in his days, Shule was grateful to God that he had been blessed with Omer and that the boy had seen peace all his young life.

"Fine, then," Ezra chimed in. "Our mighty father continued fighting to regain his kingdom and bring peace again to the land." Blocking a weak attack from young Omer, he went on. "Noah's son, Cohor, tried to carry on the war in his father's stead, but never took down the mighty Shule.'" Ezra made a move to strike Omer's left flank but, to his surprise, was blocked by a new challenger.

"Then I rebelled against the greed of my father Cohor and returned the divided kingdom to its rightful heir," Nimrod, son of Cohor, said as he smiled down at young Omer. He had sneaked into the courtyard just in time to finish the story. He was a young, handsome man, well-known and well loved throughout the kingdom. "Your father has shown me great mercy and much favor, so I will protect my king and his son." At this, Nimrod shielded Omer from his enemies and positioned himself to attack. "Even if I must do so from his own brothers!"

Nimrod and Omer laughed and lunged forward, attacking the other sons of Shule, who immediately relented, kneeling to plead for mercy from the young prince. They received none. Omer was on them at once.

As Shule watched his family around him, he thought again of the goodness of God in bringing him through so many trials in his long life. He wanted nothing more than to provide a legacy of peace and righteousness for his people—and for his faithful sons. Shule had even passed a law allowing the prophets of God to travel freely about the kingdom, and he supported them in calling the people to repentance from their iniquities and idolatries.

God prospered Shule's people and his reign, and Shule saw peace and executed judgment in righteousness all the rest of his days.

Omer grew up embracing the legacy his father and brothers had left him. The Lord blessed and preserved him and his people. The day came when treachery was reborn in the land and the pattern of bondage was renewed—but that's another story.

Endnotes

1 Traditionally, the first step in forging a sword is to form the metal into a bar or "billet."

2 Although it is not specific in Ether 7:3 that Corihor was the oldest, I consider it likely that he was. Originally, the oldest was considered for the first king among the people of Jared, but when none of the older sons of Jared or his brother would take on that mantle, one of the younger (perhaps the youngest) sons of Jared, Orihah, was anointed king (Ether 6:25–27). From then on, tradition among the Jaredites held that one of the youngest sons would inherit the throne (Ether 7:3; 7:7; 7:26; 8:1; 9:14; 9:24–25; 10:4, 14, 16; 11:4). Here then is a motivation for the oldest to make a move to take by force the kingdom that he will never inherit.

3 The scriptures give us no information on Shule's wife, except that she gave him many sons and daughters (Ether 7:14). Between the birth of Shule's first sons and the sons and daughters born to him in his old age (Ether 7:26), there seems to have been a considerable passage of time. Even though we don't know that Shule's wife was killed in the uprising of Noah, it is very possible—even probable—that Omer (who was born in Shule's old age) had a different mother than his older brothers.

4 It doesn't say explicitly that Noah slept in the royal palace, but I can't think of any reason why he wouldn't after conquering the land of Moron "where the king dwelt" (Ether 7:5, 6). I'm also assuming that the prison was either in or close to the house of the king. What really intrigues me is that Noah's new residence was probably the same one that had been Shule's. If this is the case, I feel sorry for him. Having once been a boy and being the father of boys myself, I am well aware that there could not have been any part of the royal house unknown to Shule's sons. They would have grown up exploring, laying siege to, and escaping from every room in the house. I would propose that Noah could not have a less secure house than one in which that group of boys grew up. Poor, poor Noah.

*A*midst the rise of secret combinations and greed, the Lord would protect the righteous who were led by a noble king.

2 *O*mer
The Last King Standing

❧ *Ether 8–9* ❧

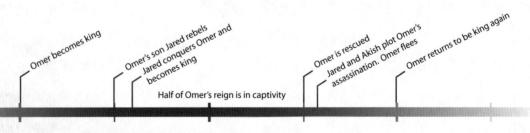

Omer becomes king

Omer's son Jared rebels

Jared conquers Omer and becomes king

Half of Omer's reign is in captivity

Omer is rescued

Jared and Akish plot Omer's assassination. Omer flees

Omer returns to be king again

Dates are not available

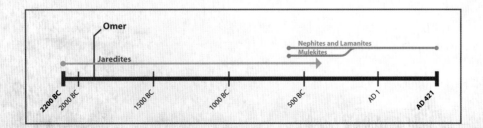

Omer

Jaredites

Nephites and Lamanites

Mulekites

2200 BC   2000 BC   1500 BC   1000 BC   500 BC   AD 1   AD 421

Omer awoke with a start, his senses alert. He could hear muffled voices and what sounded like a fight outside his home—the place that had been his prison[1] for so many years. He moved to stand, straining to interpret what was happening outside, but before he had risen to his feet, a body came smashing backward through his door. Limbs flailing, it hit the ground with a thud, then lay still.

Omer squinted in the darkness and, after a few moments of silence, tentatively moved closer to the body. When he saw the face, he recognized him as one of the guards. Then, sensing movement behind him, Omer quickly turned to see two men standing in the door frame. They were silhouetted against the night sky with weapons in their hands. Omer began shifting backward, but they advanced rapidly and knelt beside him, one reaching out to touch his shoulder.

"Father," they said together. Omer froze, staring in disbelief.

"Esrom? Coriantumr?" he whispered.

"Yes, Father," Esrom assured him, squeezing his shoulder. "You are free."

"Jared?" Omer said quietly, not quite knowing if he wanted to know what had happened.

"Being heavily guarded in the throne room." Esrom smiled as he stood and raised his father to his feet. "They are waiting for you."

Omer ascended the palace steps, accompanied by his sons as the people cried, "Hail, King Omer! The rightful king returns!" The three men strode directly toward Jared. Soldiers flanked him on all sides, steadily pointing weapons at him as he cowered on the floor. When they reached him, Omer stopped, an expression of both pity and disappointment on his face as he looked down at the man who had been the cause of so much suffering among his people for so long.

"Jared, my son," Omer began in a measured tone. "You are guilty of taking the throne by force from its rightful heir. You have dishonored your father and your God. These offenses carry the penalty of death."

Jared, once the proudest of men, put his face in his hands and wept like a child. "Please, Father, have mercy on me as the great kings of old have had on their wayward sons." A look of desperation filled his eyes, and he added, "My brothers have sought fit to spare my life that I might give back what is rightfully yours. The kingdom is in your hands. Will you not have mercy and preserve my life?"

The rightful king looked into his son's eyes, knowing that Jared's tears were being shed more for the loss of the kingdom than for fear of entering the presence of his God so woefully unprepared. Even still, Omer considered Jared's words. The great kings of old had indeed been merciful and wise. Omer's own father, Shule, had reigned in righteousness, and the Lord had blessed him greatly.

"Your younger brothers have honored you with their mercy, " Omer replied. Then, after a weighty pause, he added, "I will do the same."

Jared's joy at being spared was brief. He often thought back to the night[2] of the attack that had taken his throne, still not fully comprehending how it had all happened. He replayed the brief events, always wondering how he could have changed the outcome. But every scenario ended with him sitting on the floor of the palace throne room, his stomach twisting inside him as he waited for his father's footsteps—footsteps that would bring deliverance or death. Now he swallowed bitterly. Death would have been preferable.

Jared's daughter silently watched her father. She glanced down at the scroll[3] in her hand. Her grip on it tightened, and she smiled as she stepped from the shadows, approaching her father as he sat in a dimly lit room of his house. She was strikingly beautiful and had a love of power and talent for treachery—both gifts inherited from her father.

"Whereby hath my father so much sorrow? Hath he not read the record which our fathers brought across the great deep?" Her father barely acknowledged her presence, so she opened the scroll for him and dropped it in his lap. Jared had no interest in seeking solace in the writings of the prophets. The God of heaven was not the god he sought.

Watching her father carefully, Jared's daughter continued. "Behold, is there not an account concerning them of old," she knelt beside him and lowered her voice to barely a whisper, "that they by their secret plans did obtain *kingdoms and great glory?*" She paused and turned her father's face toward her own. He looked up slowly and met her gaze. She saw a spark of understanding in her father's eyes, and he began to smile.

Jared's daughter continued in an urgent whisper as she introduced her plan. "Therefore, let my father send for Akish, the son of Kimnor; and behold, I am fair, and I will dance before him, and I will please him, that he will desire me to wife; wherefore if he shall desire of thee that ye shall give unto him me to wife, then shall ye say: I will give her if . . ." She paused meaningfully, her eyes hard and her voice cold. "If ye will bring unto me the head of my father, Omer, the king."

The daughter of Jared had judged Akish well. He was seduced by her charms and was willing to do whatever it took to win her hand—even kill a man who had once been his friend. But he would need help to cover his tracks and ensure his protection, so in the dark of a moonless night, Akish and his kinsfolk gathered in Jared's house and swore allegiance to Akish. They vowed by heaven and earth to never divulge anything Akish revealed to them, and they received oaths the likes of which had been handed down from Cain, a murderer from the beginning. Anyone who broke the oath would lose his head.

While secret works of darkness thrived in the house of Jared, the Lord visited Omer in a dream and revealed to him that he must take his family, including all of his loyal sons and daughters, and depart out of the land.

Omer awoke with a sense of urgency. Though it was still dark, he stood and sent for his sons Coriantumr and Esrom. Omer could not sit still and wait. He began gathering clothing and belongings as best he could in the semidarkness. When they arrived, Omer paused and told them of his dream.

"Why does the Lord command us to depart out of the land?" Esrom asked when Omer had finished.

"The Lord has not given a reason," Omer responded as he folded a blanket and placed it in a bag. "My spirit has been troubled within me, but I feel the Lord's hand directing us. Please, my sons, gather our family together." He hesitated then added, "All but Jared and his family. Then let us depart. Surely the Lord will bless us for our obedience."

Some time later, laden with tents and provisions, Omer and his family departed. They traveled for many days until they reached the eastern seashore. Then, assured that they were safe, Omer's sons pitched tents, and the family settled into their new life.

Years passed,[4] and though life among Omer's people was not always easy, they were happy. One morning, Omer awoke early and walked up to a ridge that overlooked the village, as he often did, to see the sun rise above the eastern sea. He loved to see the beauty of God's creations. But this time, the view was different. When he looked behind him to the west, he saw figures moving in the distance. Omer's brow furrowed in concern. As the figures drew closer, Omer saw that there was only a small group of men. They walked slowly, as if weighed down by a burden he couldn't see. Compassion welled up in Omer's heart, and he went forward to offer them aid.

When he was close enough, he hailed the men. "I am Omer, son of Shule."

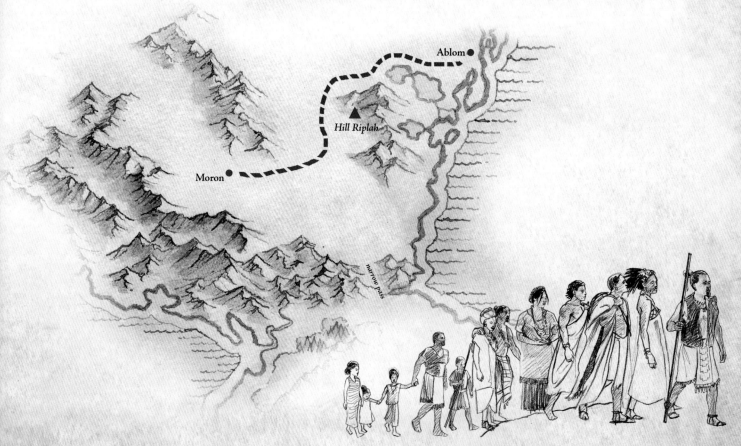

The travelers stopped in their tracks and fell to their knees. This show of obeisance surprised and puzzled Omer, who continued forward, assuring them that they could rise. But none of the young men moved until Omer raised them up one by one.

"Please, lord," said the young man who appeared to be their leader. "I am Nimrah, son of . . ." He swallowed hard and looked down before continuing. "Son of Akish, king of the land of Moron." Nimrah would not look up.

"Akish?" Omer's eyes widened. "Surely Jared is now king of Moron—he who once usurped the throne by treachery. Is this not so?"

Nimrah then lifted his head in surprise. "You have not heard? How can it be that you do not know of the darkness that has fallen over the land of Moron?"

"Come and sit," invited Omer. "Rest a moment and then tell me what has happened among that remnant of my people."

Nimrah and his men did as they were bidden. Then Nimrah looked at the king, sighed heavily, and began his story.

"There was a plot to kill thee, my lord. Jared had conspired with my father, Akish, to murder thee. Once you had departed out of the land and Jared had become king, his daughter and Akish were given to one another in marriage." He lowered his voice and continued. "But not much time had passed before my father wondered why he should not have the throne for himself. He appealed to his kinsman, those with whom he had plotted your death, and they vowed to take the life of the king."

"Jared is dead, then?" Omer inquired quietly.

"He was beheaded upon his very throne, while he sat giving audience to his people," Nimrah continued, breaking the news as gently as he could. "My father then took the throne for himself, having married into the royal family. It was not long before he began to go mad with power. He grew jealous of his own son, my brother, and locked him in prison. He . . ." Nimrah choked on his words and waited a few moments before continuing. "My father left him there to waste away on little or no food. I pleaded with him, but he would not listen to me or anyone else. My brother finally died." Nimrah looked down. He clenched his hands together and his breath quickened. "I could not stand to be in my father's presence. I am ashamed to be his son."

He gathered his composure before lifting his eyes to look at Omer once more. "I knew that my poor brother's fate would be my own if I opposed my father, so I gathered a small number of men who were of a like mind, and we fled." He shook his head and stood, unable to sit any longer. He walked a few steps and gazed back in the direction he and his brethren had come from. "The land of Moron is filled with wickedness," he said just loud enough for Omer to hear. "The people are drunk with a desire for power, just like my father. I fear they will destroy themselves with their greed and selfishness." He paused and turned back to Omer. "We did not know where else to go. We have come to you, the rightful king, in hopes that you will show us mercy. May we join with you?"

Omer looked at the young man with compassion in his gaze and said, "There is much sorrow in your countenance for one so young." He took the young man by the arm and motioned to the others. "Come with me and find rest. My people do not enjoy the comforts of palace life, but we do find happiness and peace in righteous living."

As they entered the village, they saw men and women already busy with the day's chores. The people paused and looked on curiously when they saw Omer's guests.

"My people," Omer said in a voice for all to hear. "Come and meet Nimrah, my great-grandson, and his friends."

Many years passed,[5] and Omer grew old. The size of his family had increased tremendously, and the Lord had greatly blessed them. As he looked over his people, who had gathered before him, gratitude filled his heart. He had been prompted[6] to take his people and return to the land of Moron. When he made the announcement, he saw both joy and fear in his people's eyes, but all assented. They would follow their king wherever the Lord would lead him. They began their journey home.

Everywhere they traveled, the tokens of excess and greed lay in ruin—houses, palaces, temples, and monuments. Dead bodies littered the fields all around them.

As Omer and his people approached the once great palace, a ragged band of men, women, and children[7] stepped from the shadows. Their expressions were drawn in mourning, and their bodies looked weak. The children clung to their parents. Some recognized Omer as he drew closer, and they fell to their knees, their story pouring from them before he had uttered a word.

The group recounted how, over the years, the sons of Akish had drawn away factions of the people by luring them with money. They had warred against their father for power. After many years of bitter struggle, the land was all but desolate. Only these thirty souls remained alive.

Omer looked over the forlorn citizens of Moron and said firmly, "We are all one people now." His body was bent with age, but his voice was strong and clear. "This land is our inheritance, and we will restore it to a place of peace where the Lord can prosper his people and have joy them. The Lord has declared this to be a choice land, and those who possess it must do so in His name, or they will be destroyed from off the face of it.[8] Let us strive to be worthy of the blessings of the Lord all our days."

That they did. Despite his age, Omer reigned for many years to come and anointed the son of his old age, Emer, to reign in his stead. Omer's life had been filled with captivity, betrayal, and exile, but the Lord had watched over him. God had preserved him and allowed him to see the wicked destroy themselves and the righteous rebuild the land. The people prospered, and the last years of Omer's life were filled with peace.

Epilogue

Omer's legacy continued during the reign of his son Emer. In Emer's days the people remained strong and prosperous, and Emer reigned in righteousness all his days. He was even privileged to see the premortal Christ. However, the righteous legacy of Omer and his son would not last forever. Eventually wickedness and secret combinations would again be seen in the land—but that's another story.

Endnotes

1 Ether 8:3 tells us that Omer was in "captivity," a term used throughout the Book of Mormon to indicate the loss of freedom and being ruled by an enemy. Omer was likely not shut up in a prison cell or even under house arrest, but I needed some way to show the event of his rescue by his sons, so I chose this scene.

2 Ether 8:5. I don't know of any other instance in the Book of Mormon where an army began a battle at night.

3 Ether 8:9 shows us that the Jaredites brought scriptures with them. Whether they were written on plates, tablets, or scrolls is not said. Scrolls were the best image for this telling of the story, but even if they weren't originally written on a scroll, this could be a copy made from the original.

4 Here again I made some assumptions. The time period surrounding these events is unclear. If Nimrah is the son of Akish and Jared's daughter and if when he leaves he gathers a small number of men, perhaps he was old enough to be a man (maybe twenty or thirty years old). This would mean that Omer and his people had been on the east coast for about that long. That's a long time. Perhaps Nimrah was the son of an earlier wife of Akish, in which case, less time would have passed. We just don't know, so I used a noncommittal, "time passed."

5 Ether 9:12 says that the war between Akish and his sons lasted for "many years." That war took place after Nimrah left, so I suspect it is also the right expression to use for the passage of time among Omer's people.

6 I found no indication of how Omer knew that it was time to go home, but since the Lord told him to leave, I suggest the Lord also told him that it was safe to return.

7 Ether 9:12 says that only thirty souls survived the war in the homeland. I think it's safe to say they consisted of men, women, and children. I think it is likely that they were mostly women and children.

8 Ether 9:20.

*F*or hundreds of years, no one could pass the barrier of deadly serpents—until the Lord raised up a mighty king to free the land from this curse.

3 *Righteous Lib*

Slayer of Serpents

❧ *Ether 9–10* ❧

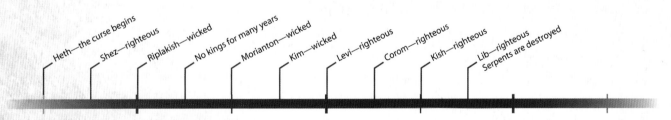

Heth—the curse begins

Shez—righteous

Riplakish—wicked

No kings for many years

Morianton—wicked

Kim—wicked

Levi—righteous

Corom—righteous

Kish—righteous

Lib—righteous Serpents are destroyed

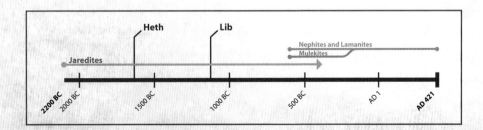

Heth

Lib

Nephites and Lamanites

Mulekites

Jaredites

2200 BC

2000 BC

1500 BC

1000 BC

500 BC

AD 1

AD 421

King Heth stumbled and fell heavily against the parched earth, grunting as his body hit the unyielding ground. He hadn't eaten in days. He knew that most were far worse off—his people were dying all around him. Shaking slightly, the king lifted his frame and began inching forward on his hands and knees, desperately hoping he might find a small morsel of food or some water that had been left behind.

His family was dead. All of them. His once-great kingdom was in ruins. His weakened body shuddered as he remembered seeing the corpses of men and beasts littering the roadside. He could not save them. Not now. His last hope—his only hope—was to reach the lands in the south. The famine was milder there, if the rumors could be believed.

"You brought this upon us." The voice that spoke was tired, sad . . . and bitter.

King Heth looked up to see a young man resting in the shade, trying to escape from the relentless sun. "Shez, my son, is that you?"[1] the king rasped, then bowed his head as a racking cough seized him. "I thought you were dead."

"You and I are all that remain of your once-royal house," Shez said. "You have murdered us all."

"Fool," King Heth spat. "What have I done that the weight of this famine should fall upon me?"

Shez stood and moved slowly toward his father, stepping forward with each word he spoke. "What have you done?" Shez stopped and looked down at his father, who was hunched over at his feet. "You butchered your father with his own sword so that you could rule this cursed land!" Shez bent over and spoke louder to ensure his father heard every word he had to say. "You had prophets of the living God thrown into pits and left to die when they warned us to repent of our wickedness! God has sent this famine to destroy us and wipe our sin from the face of this land." Shez stood then and looked away, as if he couldn't stand looking at his father's face for long.

"The punishments of God mean nothing to me," the king hissed, attempting to straighten his frame and stand but succeeding only in falling forward and hitting his knees against the ground. "I will reach the land southward, and then I will rebuild my kingdom greater than before!" Finally the king rose, his determination giving him the strength to stand.

"Do you not see the dead and rotting bodies all around you?" Shez asked. "God has cursed us with poisonous serpents that have destroyed our flocks. Even now they hedge up the way to the lands southward. I sat here to warn others who tried to pass by them. They didn't listen, and they are all dead. We are trapped here to suffer the consequences of our wickedness." He looked up into his father's face. "The only way to survive is to repent and call upon God for mercy."

"Only the weak speak of God and mercy," growled the king, then he coughed and spat upon the ground. "I am a king." Heth spoke quietly, mere inches from Shez's face "I will laugh when you die. I will thrive as your corpse rots." Heth turned and stumbled on toward the land southward.

Shez swallowed hard and watched his father for only a minute before turning slowly away to resume his journey in the opposite direction. He hadn't walked far before he heard a familiar low chorus of hiss. Then his father screamed.[2]

Those who survived humbled themselves and repented of their sins. The famine eventually ended. The generations that followed saw both wicked and righteous kings, but still the serpents remained. For more than seven generations,[3] all those who attempted to pass into the land southward fell victim to the serpents' venom. The reign of King Lib changed all that.

"It is so green here!" Hearthom said in awe as he reached out to brush his hand against the thick trunk of a tree. "Why is it so different from our home? Here, the forest seems to stretch on forever. There, we have only buildings as far as the eye can see."

"The Lord preserved this land for His people, my son." King Lib walked next to his boy and adjusted the bow strung across his son's back. Hearthom was less of a boy now and more of a young man, and he was filled with questions.[4] Lib continued. "Mine is the eighth generation[5] since the Lord separated us from this land. During that time it grew into a paradise rich with animals of the forest. Now God allows us to travel here and hunt for food."

"Why couldn't anyone come here before?" Hearthom asked, tilting his head to the side and looking up at Lib.

"You remember the stories of the great famine in the days of Heth, and of the poisonous serpents that hedged up the way to the land southward?" Lib prompted. When Hearthom nodded, he said, "Those serpents stopped the people from crossing into this land—until my day."

"What happened to the serpents?" Hearthom asked, idly poking at the foliage with his spear.

"We killed them," Lib said simply. After a moment he asked, "Why do you think we were able to destroy them when all the other generations could not?"

Hearthom jumped onto a rock, spear in hand, and raised his arms in the air before dramatically stating, "Because you are the greatest hunter of all the generations!" He launched his spear into a nearby tree trunk and then struck a pose with his arms crossed on his chest.

The king smiled a little, but his eyes were perfectly serious when he said, "No, my son.

We were able to
destroy the serpents
because God allowed us to. It
is a great blessing, and we should
always give thanks to God for it."

Hearthom nodded in understanding.
"Yes, Father." He retrieved his spear, then
turned around and said, "But the people
say you are a great hunter."

King Lib placed a hand on his son's shoulder.
"I am glad to know it, but if you are to become a
great hunter, we must stop talking and attacking
trees or we shall have no game today."

After they had walked in silence for a time, Hearthom
asked quietly, "Why can't we build a home here instead of
always traveling here to hunt?"

Before he responded, King Lib looked up at the canopy of leaves overhead, listening to
the sounds of the forest. "It is a most beautiful land," he replied. "But we must follow
the Lord's example and preserve it. Then we will always be able to hunt here and to
enjoy the splendor of God's creations."

The king was a great hunter, and they caught plentiful game that day. But the king
would have considered the trip successful even if their packs had been empty. Being
in this place with his beloved son was paradise, and his joy only grew as they traveled

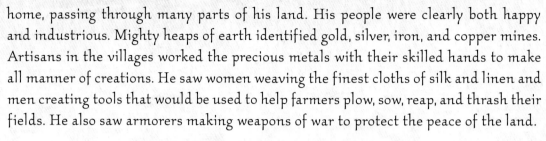

home, passing through many parts of his land. His people were clearly both happy and industrious. Mighty heaps of earth identified gold, silver, iron, and copper mines. Artisans in the villages worked the precious metals with their skilled hands to make all manner of creations. He saw women weaving the finest cloths of silk and linen and men creating tools that would be used to help farmers plow, sow, reap, and thrash their fields. He also saw armorers making weapons of war to protect the peace of the land.

When at last the king arrived at home, he was greeted by his many sons and daughters and, of course, his wife. Many years later a prophet would write of Lib's day, "And never could be a people more blessed than were they, and more prospered by the hand of the Lord. And they were in a land that was choice above all lands, for the Lord had spoken it."

To this, Lib would most certainly agree.

Endnotes

1 Although the first mention of Shez in Ether 10:1 describes him as a "descendant of Heth," the genealogy listed in Ether 1:25 identifies Shez as the son of Heth.

2 This conversation between Heth and his only surviving son is fictional, but I felt it helped to explain the background for the story of Lib and to give the reader a context in which to explain the events in the days of Heth. Although it says in Ether 10:1 that Heth died by the famine, I wondered if the serpents may have helped things along—but that's just my take on it.

3 The only person we know of among the Jaredites to give us an idea of how long a generation might be is Coriantum (Ether 9:24), who lived until he was one hundred forty-two. His wife lived to one hundred and two. If we estimate about a hundred years for each generation between Shez and Lib, perhaps the land southward had no human visitors for somewhere around seven hundred years. To put that into a modern equivalent, imagine that all the inhabitants left England after the Crusades, and no one had crossed into England's boundaries from that time to the present day. Can you imagine what an adventure it would be to explore there?

4 Hearthom appears to be a son Lib had in his old age (Ether 10:29). He would become the next king, and I created a make-believe hunting trip with the two of them to help put the reader in their present day when things were so peaceful and happy.

5 These are the generations that followed Heth and lived during the curse of the poisonous serpents, as described in Ether 10:1–18:

> 1. Shez, son of Heth—A good and righteous king.
>
> 2. Riplakish, son of Shez—A wicked and oppressive king who was killed by his own people. Ether 10:9 notes that there was then no king for many years.
>
> 3. Morianton, descendant of Riplakish—A fair king but not a righteous man.
>
> 4. Kim, son of Morianton—A wicked king who was brought into captivity by his brother.
>
> 5. Levi, son of Kim—A righteous king who lived in captivity for forty-two years before regaining the throne.
>
> 6. Corom, son of Levi—A righteous king.
>
> 7. Kish, son of Corom—No information given, but he is presumed righteous.
>
> 8. Lib, son of Kish.

Constant war and evil men threatened to devour a once-great people—and one wicked man would tower above them all.

4 Wicked Lib

The Beginning of the End of the Jaredites

❧ *Ether 13, 14* ❧

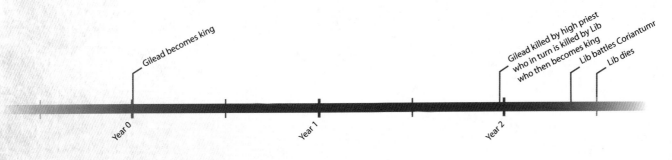

Gilead becomes king

Gilead killed by high priest who in turn is killed by Lib who then becomes king

Lib battles Coriantumr

Lib dies

Year 0

Year 1

Year 2

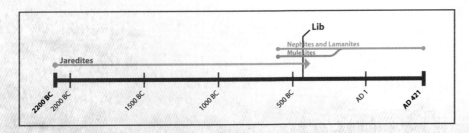

Lib

Nephites and Lamanites
Mulekites

Jaredites

2200 BC   2000 BC   1500 BC   1000 BC   500 BC   AD 1   AD 421

"Coriantumr can never be defeated!" said Helem, a soldier with a slur that betrayed just how drunk he was. "Many men have tried, and their blood now stains the land." He paused to take yet another drink from the bottle that was always by his side. "This . . . Gilead . . . is just another fool who thinks his secret brotherhood can bring down the mightiest of kings."

"Our king is only a man," Amah responded. He poked a stick into the smoldering coals of their campfire and stirred, sending a few sparks flying into the darkness. They had camped for far too long, seeing little or no action. Everyone was restless—and drunk.

"Perhaps . . ." Helem paused, scrutinizing each of his comrades carefully, the firelight sharpening the shadows on his face. "But King Coriantumr is learned in both the arts of war and the cunning of the world." He raised a hand and swept it toward the inky blackness beyond the campfire. "Look where we are now. We have surrounded Gilead and all his men here in the wilderness of Akish." Helem stood up and stumbled around the campfire before collapsing beside Amah. He offered him a swig from his bottle before clapping him on the back and saying, "Because of our great king, they have fallen into our hands." His eyes narrowed. "We will continue to lay siege to them until they perish . . . and they are helpless to stop us."

The words had scarcely left his lips when an arrow flew out of the darkness and into Helem's chest. He looked down in surprise at the shaft protruding from his body and then sunk backward. The other soldiers looked around at each other as if in a fog, failing to recognize what was happening until it was too late. Gilead and his men were upon them, and within minutes, it was over.

Gilead stood in the midst of the fallen soldiers and gathered his men together. Then he tilted his head toward the bodies of the watchmen and, with the ghost of a smile, said, "Truly, we must thank this band of Coriantumr's men for giving us a doorway out of the siege. We have been prisoners in the wilderness of Akish for far too long." He nudged a nearby body on the ground before reaching down and plucking the arrow from Helem's chest. He wiped the blood on his cloak. "Now, my brothers," he finished, raising his voice and pointing the arrow to the sky. "Let us march forth to the land of Moron! I am anxious to see my new throne."

Gilead and his army marched to the palace in Moron, and there Gilead placed himself upon the throne, declaring his reign as king over all the land. Coriantumr and his men were banished to the wilderness of Akish, and they remained there for the next two years. The unseated king was far from idle. He recruited men and added great strength to his armies, all while watching and waiting for his chance to take back his throne.

"Coriantumr is a fool!" King Gilead shouted without caring who heard. "All I had to do was march on the capital city and place myself upon the throne. Now I am king!"

"Be careful, my lord," Heslon, Gilead's high priest, said from his seat near the throne. "Remember that Shared, thy brother, was also once victorious over Coriantumr—and now he is dead."

"Don't try to frighten me," Gilead shot back, slouching lazily on his throne. "I have already held this kingdom twice as long as my brother.[1] And do not forget, priest, that I continue to receive great strength to my army because of our brotherhood."[2]

Heslon nodded. "Our brotherhood has indeed made you strong . . ." he said, his voice lowering as he slowly moved behind Gilead. His eyes narrowed underneath an elaborate headdress. "But . . . have they offered you security?" The high priest's voice was nearly a whisper, as if his words were intended for Gilead's ears only.

Gilead laughed arrogantly, though the sound was weak as it echoed in the great hall. He turned to address his court and issued a challenge: "As I sit upon this throne, is there any who dares oppose me?"

Before anyone could respond, the high priest slit an unsuspecting Gilead's throat. A small gurgle escaped Gilead's lips, and then it was over. By the time the others in the throne room realized what had happened, Heslon was looming over the body of their now-dead king.

"You are not the only one among our brotherhood who seeks for power, Gilead. And you are not the one who deserves to rule this people."

Heslon held his bloody knife and cast his gaze over the assembly, daring them to challenge him. No one did. He turned and moved quickly back toward the throne where, on the far wall, there stood a statue of no particular interest. He slid it away from the wall and disappeared into an opening revealed in the space behind it.[3]

The high priest grinned as he moved though the secret passages that stretched beneath the palace complex. "Soon all will bow down to me," he whispered under his breath, pleased that everything had gone according to his plan. He looked down for a moment to wipe his bloody hands on his robe, but just then the light around him seemed to dim. He quickly looked up to see the passage ahead blocked by a massive figure.

A powerful hand shot out, squeezing Heslon's neck and bringing him to his knees. He looked up at the towering form above him and caught the briefest glimpse of light reflecting off a dark blade. The towering shadow spoke in a quiet but deadly voice.

"I am called Lib, but now you may call me your king, *brother!*" The knife flashed in the dim light, and the priest fell, lifeless, to the ground.

It was not long before word of political instability in the land of Moron reached Coriantumr in the wilderness of Akish. With the erratic shifts of power within the secret combinations, he decided it was time to retake his throne. Coriantumr prepared his men to take back their land, and they began their march toward the land of Moron.

As Coriantumr and his army at last reached the borders of Moron, he signaled for his men to quicken their march. However, as they came to the summit of the hilltop, Coriantumr cursed beneath his breath. Before him stood an army, and at its head stood the new king, Lib.

Even Coriantumr, who had faced many mighty warriors in his life, was unnerved as Lib stepped forward. Lib was by far the largest man he had ever seen—surely no one in all the land could match him for stature. Steeling himself, Coriantumr set his jaw and thrust his fist into the air as he raised the battle cry.

Steel swords broke through wooden shields and smashed against breastplates of copper and brass. Coriantumr and Lib fought in the midst of the tumult. Lib wielded his strength like an avalanche, crashing through Coriantumr's defenses. The old king was no match for Lib's strength, but, as an experienced fighter, Coriantumr did not depend on brute force alone.

On Lib's next strike, Coriantumr raised his shield to block it, but as the sword struck he offered no resistance, forcing Lib to overextend. Coriantumr used the momentum to rotate around and strike Lib's flank, intending to inflict a death blow. But to his surprise, Lib did not lose his balance. Instead he also rotated around, and his sharp blade flashed toward Coriantumr's outstretched arm. Coriantumr stumbled backward, clutching the wound. As Lib advanced to deliver the final blow, a wave of Coriantumr's men surged forward, pushing Lib back into the fray. Coriantumr lay on the ground for a moment, dazed by the speed and prowess of his nemesis. He tore part of his tunic, wrapped his arm, and charged back into the battle.

Coriantumr's men fought with renewed strength, compelling Lib and his army to flee before them. Only when Lib's army reached the borders by the seashore were they forced to halt. With the endless sea at their backs, Lib's men fought with a desperate resolve, pushing back against the relentless forces of Coriantumr.

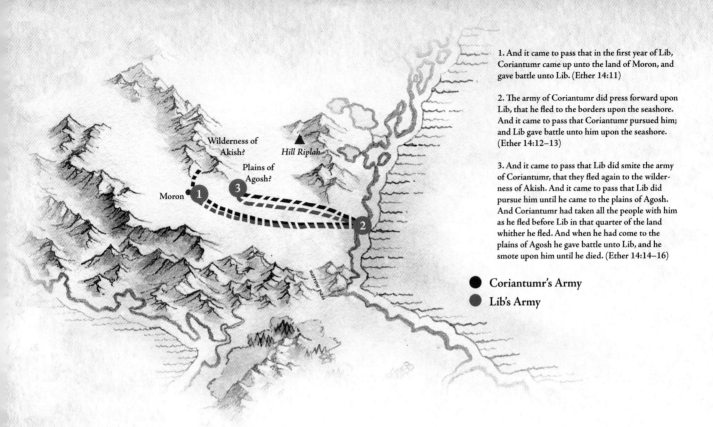

1. And it came to pass that in the first year of Lib, Coriantumr came up unto the land of Moron, and gave battle unto Lib. (Ether 14:11)

2. The army of Coriantumr did press forward upon Lib, that he fled to the borders upon the seashore. And it came to pass that Coriantumr pursued him; and Lib gave battle unto him upon the seashore. (Ether 14:12–13)

3. And it came to pass that Lib did smite the army of Coriantumr, that they fled again to the wilderness of Akish. And it came to pass that Lib did pursue him until he came to the plains of Agosh. And Coriantumr had taken all the people with him as he fled before Lib in that quarter of the land whither he fled. And when he had come to the plains of Agosh he gave battle unto Lib, and he smote upon him until he died. (Ether 14:14–16)

● **Coriantumr's Army**
● **Lib's Army**

"My king!" Cohor[4], one of Coriantumr's captains shouted as he ran toward Coriantumr. "He's broken our lines! Our men are giving way. What shall we do?"

Coriantumr looked at his weary and thinning ranks. He had expected to crush the upstart king's forces by now. He thought for only a moment before giving his order. "Pull our men back."

"My lord?" questioned Cohor. He had rarely heard his king call for a retreat.

Coriantumr smiled but wasn't willing to share his thoughts just yet. "Trust me, Cohor. Tell the men that the king commands we return to the wilderness of Akish!"

And so the men of Coriantumr fled, but they stopped at almost every village and settlement along the way. Lib assumed they sought refuge, but he had no intention of letting them rest. He pursued them until they were stopped at the plains of Agosh. To his surprise, the army of Coriantumr was waiting for him. For the first time, Lib noticed how much Coriantumr's army had grown. Unbeknownst to Lib, Coriantumr had been gathering people to his banner as he fled.[5] Now his army was revitalized with fresh troops, while the men of Lib suffered weariness and fatigue.

Before Lib could assess or fully comprehend the strength of the army before him, the enemy raised a battle cry. Coriantumr led the charge, falling upon Lib with renewed vigor. His strokes hit Lib like a hammer. Again and again he struck.

"Did you think me too old and frail?" shouted Coriantumr as he dodged a wild strike from Lib and sliced a gash in the giant man's leg. Lib cried out in pain and frustration.

"War has been my companion all my days. All those who have challenged me are dead!" Coriantumr locked his shield around Lib's, delivering a stunning blow to Lib's head and wrenching his shield from his grasp. Casting it aside, the old king stood over Lib's battered and bloodied form.

"I have fought much and bled much, but even if all this land is destroyed, I will remain standing! Take that prophecy to your grave!" Coriantumr's sword was swift and deadly, but Lib managed four haunting last words.

"I will be avenged . . ."

As Coriantumr stumbled away from Lib's corpse, another man approached it reverently. This man, almost equal in stature to the fallen, knelt and looked over the body of his brother. Slowly the deep-set eyes lifted, glaring at the withdrawing form of Coriantumr. The grim warrior, whose name was Shiz, swore an oath in his heart[6] that he would not rest until he had avenged his brother's blood by taking Coriantumr's life—even if they were the last two men left in the land—but that's another story.

Endnotes

1 Ether 13:23–24. It seems that Gilead's brother, Shared, held the kingdom for a year or less before Coriantumr's sons took it back for their father. Gilead held it for about two years before he lost it.

2 The record never explicitly states that the high priest was "one of the secret combinations," but the fact that he knows about a secret pass (Ether 14:10) and that he was chosen to be Gilead's high priest leads me to believe he was also part of that power-hungry, murderous group. Another possibility is that the high priest was part of Coriantumr's inner circle and was left behind at the palace and made to serve the new king, Gilead. Assassinating Gilead would have been a sign of his loyalty to Coriantumr, but his treason would certainly have brought about his slaying by Lib (another member of the secret combination) (Ether 14:10). I think it's likely that Gilead would have surrounded himself with the most trusted members of his secret combination. If that's true, it didn't work out very well for him in the end.

3 In truth, we have no idea if there was a secret entrance to the secret pass (Ether 14:10), but the nature of the "secret pass" is unclear, so it is possible. It could have been outside, like an alley or valley (Mosiah 22:7 seems be referencing something like this), but I like to think of it as a tunnel. A friend of mine took a tour of Monte Albán in Oaxaca during his mission in Mexico and saw (and climbed through) a secret tunnel. They were apparently used so that the priest could "magically" appear at the top of a temple. Regardless of which option is right, both are possible, and I prefer the tunnel scenario.

4 Cohor is mentioned as a contemporary of Coriantumr, but nothing more is said other than that he is unrepentant, as are his children. Why he should be mentioned by name is unclear. It seems likely to me that he is one of the men fighting against Coriantumr in the context of Ether 13:15–17. But without knowing for sure, I made him a captain in Coriantumr's army. I hope he doesn't mind.

5 Ether 14:15.

6 I added this thought for Shiz, since it hearkens to the attitude he has toward Coriantumr that we see later on in Ether 15:28.

Nephites and Lamanites
The Journey Begins

There is probably no more frequently told story from the Book of Mormon than that of Lehi, his family, and their journey to the promised land.

Lehi was called as a prophet to warn Jerusalem of impending destruction around 600 BC during the reign of King Zedekiah. His message of repentance was not well received, and he soon found his life threatened by the very people he was trying to save. In a vision, he was commanded to take his family and flee Jerusalem. The Lord sent Lehi's sons back to Jerusalem on two separate occasions—first to retrieve the brass plates (a sacred record of scripture and genealogy), and second to convince a righteous man named Ishmael and his wife and children to join them on their journey. Before their eight-year trek into the unknown wilderness, the Lord gave Lehi a special compass called the Liahona. With this tool the Lord led them through the wilderness and eventually across the sea to the promised land (the Americas).

Among all of Lehi's sons born in Jerusalem, none was more faithful than Nephi. The two oldest, Laman and Lemuel, were a murmuring and rebellious lot. The conflicts and hardships of the journey could often be traced to them. Two other sons were born to Lehi during their journey in the wilderness—Jacob and Joseph. Both became righteous men who followed the example of Nephi.

Lehi did not live long after their arrival in the promised land. After his death, Nephi and those who wished to follow the path of righteousness (Nephites), separated from Laman and his followers (Lamanites) for their own safety. The Lamanites lived in the lands of their first inheritance, and the Nephites lived in a place they called the land of Nephi. After many generations, the Nephites were forced to leave and find a new home in the lands to the north.

※

Mulekites
Descendants of a Jewish King

Unbeknownst to the Nephites and Lamanites, just to the north lived another group that had come from Jerusalem at the end of King Zedekiah's reign. Not long after Lehi left, the Babylonians attacked Jerusalem, and King Zedekiah was captured. His sons were rounded up and slain in front of him, and then his eyes were put out before he was carried away captive to Babylon, which is where he lived for the rest of his life (2 Kings 25:7). But one son—Mulek— escaped (Helaman 8:21).

The scriptures are silent about how old Mulek was, how he escaped, and who he brought with him. We do not know how he was led to the promised land. What we do know is that Mulek and those who followed him journeyed in the wilderness of the old world, were led by the hand of the Lord to the new world, and did not bring any written records with them (Omni 1:16–17).

We also know that the Lord brought them into the northern lands (Helaman 6:10) around the land of Desolation. After first landing there, they traveled into the south wilderness and remained there from that point on (Alma 22:30–31; Omni 1:16). Today, we sometimes refer to the descendants of Mulek (and those who followed him) as "Mulekites," but the Book of Mormon refers to them as the "people of Zarahemla," presumably named after their leader at the time they were first discovered by the Nephites (Omni 1:14, Mosiah 25:2). The land of Zarahemla became the new home to the Nephites in the days of King Mosiah—but that's another story.

The land of Nephi had been their home for generations, but a righteous leader would lead his people to a new home. Nothing could prepare them for what they would find.

5 *Mosiah*
The First King of Zarahemla

❖ *Omni 1* ❖

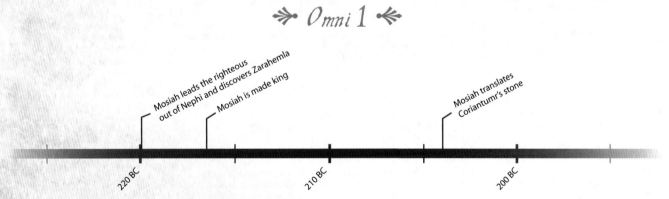

Mosiah leads the righteous out of Nephi and discovers Zarahemla

Mosiah is made king

Mosiah translates Coriantumr's stone

220 BC

210 BC

200 BC

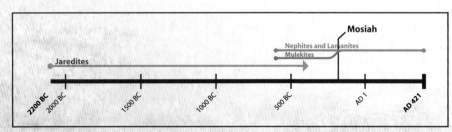

Mosiah

Nephites and Lamanites
Mulekites

Jaredites

2200 BC
2000 BC

1500 BC

1000 BC

500 BC

AD 1

AD 421

"My prince," Amaleki gasped. "Your father is dead, and the Lamanites are within the city walls. We must leave—now!" He was seconds away from grabbing hold of Mosiah's robe and dragging him to safety if the prince[1] did not follow.

"This way," Mosiah said quietly, placing a hand on his friend's shoulder. He quickly led the way deeper into the palace complex.

Thick plumes of smoke billowed into the sky, blocking out the sun's light and darkening the corridors and courtyards as they ran. The city was ablaze, and the riotous sounds of battle[2] drew ever closer.

As they rounded a corner, Mosiah suddenly stopped at the entrance of a narrow chamber. "Wait," he called out to Amaleki, and he turned to enter the door.

In desperation, Amaleki took hold of Mosiah's arm and waved his hand toward the blackened, noonday sky. "We can't wait! If we don't leave now, all is lost!"

Mosiah stopped immediately, his massive form looming before Amaleki. A piercing intensity lit his eyes as he looked toward his loyal friend. "I will not leave without the artifacts that are most sacred to our people. Have you made safe your charge?"

Amaleki[3] lowered his gaze and nodded. As one of the priestly lineage from the loins of Jacob, son of Lehi, he understood well the vitality of preserving both the sacred records and artifacts. Like those who had come before him, he had sworn an oath to care for and protect the writings contained in the plates of Nephi[4].

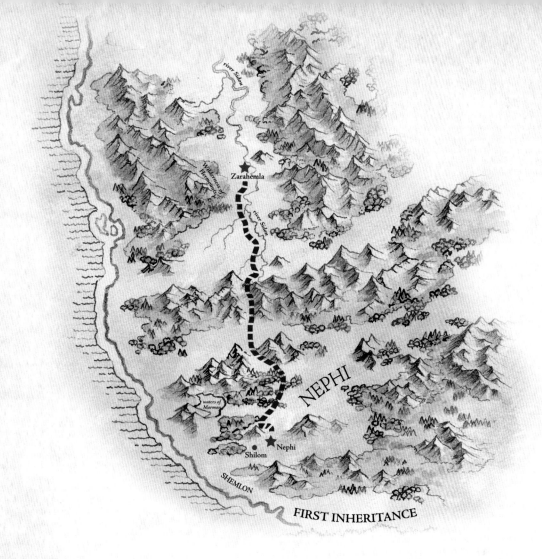

"Then help me carry the rest," Mosiah pleaded. He moved through the entryway and into the dimly lit chamber beyond. The room would be easily overlooked by most, but what it held was of greater value than the rest of the palace combined—at least to the people of God, it was. Amaleki swallowed his fear of the encroaching Lamanite army and followed the prince to where he knelt beside the most prized possessions the Nephites—the Liahona, the sword of Laban, the brass plates, and the record of the kings engraved on the large plates of Nephi.

Though burdened by their treasured cargo, Amaleki and Mosiah quickly made their way to the outskirts of the besieged capital. Once outside the city walls, they traveled west through the forest until they reached the base of a great hill. There the two men fell to the earth in exhaustion.

"How many are here?" Mosiah asked, panting heavily. He gently dropped his load to the ground and wiped the sweat from his brow as he looked up, trying to view the summit ahead.

"As many as would hearken to the voice of the Lord," Amaleki replied. He'd also set his load on the ground for a brief moment to catch his breath. He slowly rose to his feet once more. "They prepared for their journey into the wilderness as best they could."

After another moment's rest, Mosiah and Amaleki picked up their cargo and began to climb. As they neared the top, a voice rang out. "Identify yourselves!"

"We are friends, Zeniff[5]—and brothers in Christ!" Mosiah, stumbling with fatigue, answered the young watchman. Zeniff rushed forward to help the two men with their packs, and soon others appeared to help. Amaleki doubled over, breathing heavily. He finally gave up and collapsed to the earth in gratitude to his God. The sacred artifacts of the Nephites were safe—for now, at least.

People of all ages began flooding down the hill to offer their assistance, all while keeping their eyes peeled for enemies lurking in the lands round about them. When at last they reached the summit, the sun was only just beginning to set, but an ominous glow radiated from the south. "The city of Shilom is ablaze," Mosiah said softly, unable to keep the sorrow from his voice.

The survivors on the hill gazed at the burning city and finally succumbed to the horrifying reality of their situation. They mourned for the loss of their nation and the land that had been their home for so many generations. Many wept for the loss of loved ones, but even more than that, the survivors lamented the wickedness of their brothers and sisters, which had brought this catastrophic destruction upon them. For now, Mosiah would not restrain his tears.

After a moment, a haunting voice broke through the sounds of mourning. Amaleki stood slightly apart from the others, his voice filled with such melancholy that, at first, Mosiah failed to recognize it.

"Our lives passed away like as it were unto us a dream, we being a lonesome and a solemn people, wanderers, cast out from Jerusalem, born in tribulation, in a wilderness, and hated of our brethren, which caused wars and contentions; wherefore, we did mourn out our days."[6]

They fell silent as Amaleki looked over what remained of a once-great nation. "These are the words of my forefather, Jacob, son of Lehi. As the Lord brought to pass in the days of Lehi at Jerusalem, He has brought to pass with us this day."

The reverent stillness was broken only by the distant sounds of battle floating up through the darkness.

"This hill will be a resort[7] to us tonight," Mosiah began. "And on the morrow, when we will depart into the wilderness, the Lord, our God, will lead us."

Though traveling through the highland wilderness was treacherous, the humble group pressed onward. The comforts of the life they had left behind were a stark contrast to the suffering they now endured, and the provisions they had brought for their journey soon seemed insufficient. Some members of the party were elderly and infirm, some were children, and some were women who were with child. During their many days[8] of travel, the group found comfort in the scriptures and the prophecies of their leaders, which lightened their burdens and strengthened them. They were especially mindful of the stories of Lehi and his family in the wilderness and prayed that the Lord would likewise take them to a promised land.

"Mosiah, come! I found something you must see!" Zeniff cried as he rushed into camp. The weary travelers were just now rising to begin preparations for the day's travel. Fires were brought back to life, and what meager food still remained was carefully rationed out. Zeniff's excitement so early in the morning seemed, to some, almost unforgivable.

Mosiah drew back the flap of his tent, shaking his head and smiling, "Zeniff, do you ever sleep?" He stretched and looked up toward the sky. "Help me get the camp moving, and then we'll take a look at whatever you've found." Mosiah turned toward the nearest fire pit where a young boy was struggling to rekindle a flame. He bent down to assist him.

Undeterred, Zeniff pointed quickly toward the west. "Mosiah, please." He rushed over to Mosiah's side. "You will want to see this." A soberness had crept into the young man's voice, which made the prince hesitate and look west. Taking his silence as acceptance, Zeniff smiled and turned on his heel, shouting, "Follow me!"

The young scout led Mosiah through the forest and toward a steep ravine. Zeniff traveled quickly, at times rushing far enough ahead that Mosiah would lose sight of him. "We're almost there," he cried, disappearing from view once more as Mosiah made his way through a thick stand of trees.

Mosiah heard the unmistakable rush of a waterfall. When at last he caught sight of Zeniff again, the young man was standing on a rocky outcropping near a stunning cascade of water, which continued a great distance below where they stood.

"It flows to a river," Zeniff announced breathlessly, raising his voice so he could be heard over the pounding water. He climbed nimbly over the cliff they were standing on and urged Mosiah to follow. "The river flows out of these hills and into a great valley." He pointed to a distant, shimmering ribbon of water that snaked through the landscape before them. "And in that valley," he paused and lowered his voice a little, "I am almost certain I see a settlement."

Mosiah stared at Zeniff for a few moments and then squinted as he searched the outstretched valley. He could barely follow the path of the river, and he certainly saw no settlement. "Are you sure that's what you see?"

Zeniff turned to his leader with a hopeful smile. "Almost certain," he repeated.

Anticipation filled the camp as Mosiah and his faithful followers traveled out of the mountains and into a vast lowland valley. After several days of following the river, the landscape began to clear. Forests were replaced by farmland, and they soon found themselves on the outskirts of a large settlement.[9]

As they walked through the settlement, local villagers began following their group, smiling and speaking animatedly among themselves. They seemed anxious to communicate, but it soon became clear that the travelers and villagers spoke very different languages. As Mosiah and his followers reached the city center, a man in fine clothing who appeared to be a leader of the settlement stepped forward to meet them.

"Zarahemla" he said,[10] gesturing to himself and then to all the land round about him.

"Mosiah," said the prince in kind. He called for his men to bring forth the plates of brass. He was eager to find a way to communicate with these people and hoped maybe a written language would help. As Amaleki came forward and revealed these sacred plates, cries of excitement[11] and rejoicing rose up among the villagers. Mosiah smiled slightly, unsure of what it meant but intent on finding out.

The people of Zarahemla had no written records, and Mosiah's people began the arduous task of teaching them the Nephite language so that the scriptures could be available to all. Though much time passed before the people could communicate clearly with one another, the people of Zarahemla were overjoyed with their new guests and welcomed them into the land. The

industrious Nephites in turn helped work the land for farming and assisted their new friends in any way they could. When at last the Nephites and the people of Zarahemla began to speak the same language, the mystery of their past began to unfold.

Zarahemla gathered Mosiah and Amaleki together and slowly, in the Nephite language, said, "Many years ago my people came from a land far across the great sea. It was called Jerusalem."

"But that is not possible," Amaleki whispered, turning to Mosiah, his eyes wide with surprise.

"Incredible," Mosiah added in wonder. Silence followed for a few moments before Mosiah turned to Zeniff and said, "But if the Lord could preserve our fathers from the destruction of Jerusalem, why not others?"

Zarahemla listened to the conversation before looking at Mosiah in disbelief. "You know Jerusalem?"

Mosiah nodded and said, "My people also came from Jerusalem many years ago. The Lord led our fathers out of that land to save them from destruction. They wandered in the wilderness for a long time before being brought to this land."

The great chief did not respond for a few moments, as if searching for the words he wanted to say. Finally, with a quavering voice, he replied, "That is just as it was with our fathers. But you say that your fathers escaped before the destruction?"

"Yes," Mosiah said, waiting for the chief to continue.

Zarahemla bowed his head and spoke quietly. "Our fathers lived through the very destruction you describe. People were being killed all around them or taken prisoner. My people left to save the prince, King Zedekiah's only surviving son, Mulek, before he could be murdered as his brothers were."

Amaleki stepped forward, his eyes shining. "Our people must have left only a short time[12] before yours," he exclaimed. "Our great God led both our peoples to this land, and now, after so many generations have passed away, He has brought us together again. This can only be the work of the Almighty."

Zarahemla nodded but looked as if he did not understand Amaleki's words. "Truly our fathers must have come from the same place," he said, but he paused before asking, "But . . . who is God?"

Amaleki looked to Mosiah in confusion. The prince asked quietly, "Was it not God who led your people to this land?"

"I do not know of such a being," Zarahemla answered honestly.

Mosiah and Amaleki looked at one another, suddenly understanding why they had seen no synagogues, churches, or temples in the land. How had this people forgotten the very God who had brought them across the great deep?

The men talked all that day and long into the night. The ancestors of Zarahemla and his people had indeed come out of Jerusalem, but they had brought no written record with them. Over time, their language and their religion had become corrupted. Now the people of Zarahemla knew little of what had happened after Mulek and his people had left Jerusalem, only that they had wandered in the wilderness before crossing the great waters and arriving in this land. Mosiah assured Zarahemla and his people that God had brought Mulek's people here, and he spent much time teaching them about the Lord and His divine purposes.

"This record contains some of the words of Lehi, a prophet of God from Jerusalem." Amaleki brought forth the plates of Nephi, lifting open the golden pages, which shone in an almost heavenly light by the fire.

Mosiah took the plates, turned to the page he was looking for, and read, "Wherefore, I, Lehi, prophesy according to the workings of the Spirit which is in me, that there shall none come into this land save they shall be brought by the hand of the Lord."[13]

He paused before adding, "Our father Lehi spoke from experience, for it was he who led our people out of that wicked city so many years ago and brought them to this promised land." The prince looked at Zarahemla to make sure he understood. "And to those God leads—like you and your people—He makes a promise."

Turning back to the plates, he read, "Wherefore, I, Lehi, have obtained a promise, that inasmuch as those whom the Lord God shall bring out of the land of Jerusalem shall keep his commandments, they shall prosper upon the face of this land; and they shall be kept from all other nations, that they may possess this land unto themselves. And if it so be that they shall keep his commandments they shall be blessed upon the face of this land, and there shall be none to molest them, nor to take away the land of their inheritance; and they shall dwell safely forever."[14]

The men sat in silence for several minutes after Mosiah had finished reading. It was clear from Zarahemla's reverent expression that he was deeply moved by what he was learning. The Spirit of the Lord testified to each person's heart of the truthfulness of those words.[15]

Zarahemla and Mosiah continued their discussion for several days. Zarahemla revealed what he could of his people's oral tradition, including the genealogy of his fathers. Mosiah recorded all his words on the plates of Nephi, the record of the kings.

When Zarahemla called for his people to gather together, the people of Mosiah responded as well. With each passing day, the Nephite refugees and the people of Zarahemla were becoming one people. They shared food and skills, and they worked together in the fields and in the markets. Today's announcement would only serve to make official their already blossoming unity.

"My people!" Zarahemla called out in a grand voice for all to hear. "These travelers from the south wilderness have brought great joy to our people. They have taught me that our ancestors were brought to this land by the hand of a loving God. Through the years we have seen many wars and contentions among our people, which have threatened our peace. Mosiah's record teaches us that if we keep the commandments of the God who created us all, He will protect us, and we will be blessed in this land."

Many in the crowd clapped their hands in joy, for the people of Zarahemla had already begun learning about God from their new neighbors, and they were anxious to know more of Him. Drawing on the crowd's approval, Zarahemla continued.

"Just as in times of old, God has led a prophet out of a wicked city and into a promised land. Mosiah is God's prophet, and he has been led here, bringing with him a good and skilled people. We all know this to be true." Many in the crowd nodded and smiled at his words, and Zarahemla went on, his voice fervent. "He has brought written records with him, which are most precious. With them he can trace his royal ancestry from generation to generation. He carries a sword unlike any we have ever beheld and a compass that, through the power of God, directed his ancestors to this land. I know that by the power of this same God and His holy prophet we can be a mighty nation, a peaceful nation, and a godly nation!"

With each word he spoke the cheering grew louder as the people began to understand their leader's vision. They could become something more than they had ever been.

"So I ask you, my brethren and my sisters," Zarahemla concluded, "will you have Mosiah to be your king and unite with his people?" His words

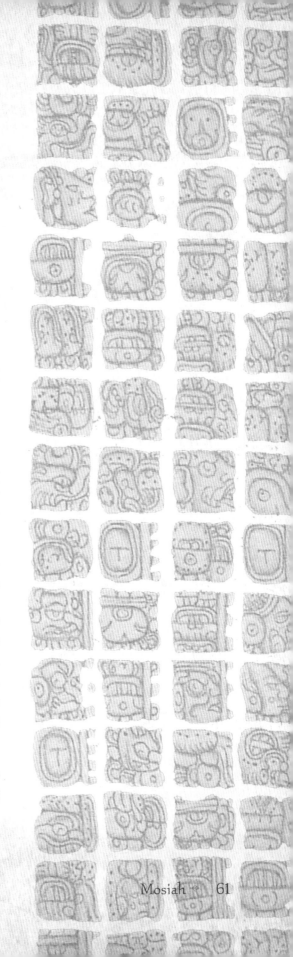

were again met with an enthusiastic cheer of approval. Zarahemla stepped aside, gesturing for Mosiah to join him. "Then we will no longer be two separate nations. We are one people gathered under the banner of our great king—King Mosiah!"

Celebrations in the land of Zarahemla continued all that day, ringing in a new era of peace and prosperity. Mosiah was indeed a good and just king, and the teachings of God did much to unify the people. He marveled at the goodness of God in reuniting his people with their brethren of the tribes of Israel. But even more marvels were yet to be seen.

Not long after King Mosiah had begun his reign, he learned that in the northern part of the land, by the seashore, the people of Zarahemla kept a large stone, which was covered with engravings that no one could read. The stone had been kept there for generations, and tradition held that it had once belonged to an ancient king.[16]

The day the stone was brought to him, King Mosiah looked on it with wonder. Amaleki stood by his side. He sat with his chin resting on his palm, studying the intricate engravings that were carved onto the surface of the curious stone. He had truly never seen anything like them. Those who kept the stone had also brought a few other items that were said to have also belonged to the mysterious king. Mosiah turned to examine the ancient royal vestment, a breastplate, and a small bundle. He picked up the bundle and held his breath as he unwrapped the covering. The two stones were smooth and clear— beautiful in their simplicity.

"I've read about these from the brass plates," the king whispered reverently. "I never thought to see them in my lifetime."

Mosiah did not know how a Urim and Thummim[17] had come into this land, but as he turned back to the great stone, he was filled with the Spirit of revelation and was able to use them to interpret the engravings.

"What do you see?" Amaleki asked upon seeing Mosiah's expression.

"This stone gives an account of one Coriantumr and his people, who were all slain. Coriantumr dwelt among the people of Zarahemla for nine months." Mosiah was perfectly still as he continued to read.

Though hesitant to interrupt again, Amaleki braved another query. "Where did he come from?"

Mosiah looked up in amazement. "This people lived originally in the days of the Tower of Babel, when God confounded the people's language."

"That was thousands of years ago,"[18] Amaleki whispered incredulously. "What happened to them?"

Mosiah sighed. "The information is very scarce. The record states only that the judgments of God fell upon them, and now their bones lay scattered in the land northward."

A somber silence fell over the room. When Amaleki spoke his voice held an edge of sarcasm, "That's a terrible ending."

Mosiah smiled and clapped his hand firmly on his dear friend's shoulder. "Then let us take care that it does not happen to us."

And so began a nation whose greatness would usher in some of the most righteous leaders and prophets of the Book of Mormon. It would be to this nation that, not many generations from the days of Mosiah, the Savior of the world would appear and change their world for hundreds of years to come.

Not everyone was happy to remain in the land of Zarahemla, however. Many wished to retake the royal city in the land of Nephi—the city of the fathers. In no time preparations were made to do just that—but that's another story.

Endnotes

1 Who was Mosiah? The strongest evidence links him to the royal lineage of the Nephites even though he is not referred to as "king" until he reigns over the people in the land of Zarahemla.

Important points to consider:

- He was in possession of the sacred objects held by the kings: the brass plates, sword of Laban, Liahona, and the record of the kings. These items continued to be passed on from king to king (Words of Mormon 1:10). The scriptures say that the Lord sent the brass plates (and presumably the other items as well) with the people of Mosiah (Omni 1:14). How could he have access to these items if he was not part of the royal house? Maybe the Lord made special arrangements for Mosiah to obtain the plates like he did for Nephi (1 Nephi 4).

- It makes sense that the people of Zarahemla might appoint Mosiah king (they don't seem to have had a king of their own) if he had a royal lineage and had the records to prove his claim.

- Mormon tells us that the record of the kings, which King Benjamin (Mosiah's son) was in possession of, had been, "handed down by the kings, from generation to generation until the days of king Benjamin" (Words of Mormon 1:10). So it seems likely that Mosiah was in possession of the records because he was the king of the Nephites before their flight into the wilderness (or in line for the throne).

The most logical conclusion for me is that Mosiah was the righteous heir to the Nephite throne who was warned of the Lord to flee. For some reason, his father couldn't accompany him, but knowing that destruction awaited the people in the land of Nephi, he handed the records and sacred items to Mosiah to care for and to take with him. Whatever Mosiah's history, the fact remains that it was his faithfulness that allowed him to lead the righteous people out of the land and save the Nephites from total destruction.

2 There is no clear answer in the account in Omni regarding the conditions when Mosiah led the people out of the land of Nephi. I have decided to set the scene during a battle based on the hint in Omni 1:12 that the Lord warned Mosiah to flee out of the land. Also, in Mosiah 11:13 we learn that Mosiah and his followers used the hill north of Shilom as a resort during their flight. The word *resort* is mentioned elsewhere in the Book of Mormon only in association with places of protection from enemies (see Mosiah 18:5; Alma 48:5, 8; 52:6). It is also possible that the enemies Mosiah was fleeing from were, in fact, his own people, the Nephites.

3 Deciding which record keeper would be part of this exodus was a bit tricky. Of those few who have tried to work out a timeline for this period of Nephite history (the most well-known being John W. Welch, *Charting the Book of Mormon*) all seem to suggest that it was Abinadom (the father of Amaleki) who journeyed with Mosiah to discover the land of Zarahemla. I think there is a strong case for Amaleki. Allow me to try to offer explanation for both candidates, Abinadom and Amaleki, and show why I have chosen to go with Amaleki:

Who left on the exodus with Mosiah in the care of the small plates of Nephi?

ABINADOM:

When working out the timeline, I have used the proposed 130 B.C. as the closing of the events in Omni (i.e., the death of Amaleki), and 200 B.C. as the time when Zeniff returned to the land of Nephi. If we assume that the exodus took place maybe ten years before that, and if we assume that a young Amaleki of perhaps twenty-five was given responsibility of the plates, this puts Amaleki's age of death at more than one hundred years old. That is pretty old compared to the ages that we know about for certain among the Nephites, e.g. Alma (82), Mosiah (63—Mosiah 29:45-46), and Mormon, who died between 74 and 90 years of age (Mormon 1-8:5). The more likely choice would be that Abinadom left on the exodus and that Amaleki was born later.

Omni 1:23 states that Amaleki was "born in the days of Mosiah." The more common use of the phrase, "in the days of" seems to indicate, "during the reign of" or "during the ministry of." Therefore, Amaleki would not be born until Mosiah was anointed king and, according to our record, that happened after the exodus. "In the days of Mosiah" could also refer to his ministry among his people, warning them of the coming destruction, but if Amaleki was born during this time it would still likely make him too young to be the official caretaker of the small plates.

AMALEKI:

It's a less common meaning, but one can interpret, "in the days of" to mean "during the life of" or "within the lifetime of." If we take this view, Amaleki could have been born within the lifetime of Mosiah (Omni 1:23). It still likely means that he was born during Mosiah's presence in public life, but this does not have to mean that Mosiah was king. Indeed, Mosiah was such a major figure that perhaps being associated with any part of his life was worth mentioning.

The strongest reason I have for choosing Amaleki as the keeper of the plates is that his father, Abinadom, ended the short verses he wrote by saying that he knew of no new revelation or prophesy other than that which has been written already (Omni 1:11). If Abinadom had lived to be part of the exodus out of the land of Nephi, he would have been part of one of the most significant revelations to happen in hundreds of years. Mosiah declares that the Lord revealed to him that they must flee from homes they had lived in for nearly four centuries to be led in the wilderness by "many preachings and prophesyings" (Omni 1:12–13) to discover a new remnant of the tribes of Israel (Zarahemla was a descendant of Mulek who was of the tribe of Judah (Mosiah 25:2; Helaman 8:21; Jeremiah 1:3). Doesn't it seem odd that this doesn't merit a mention in the record of Abinadom? Perhaps he was not a righteous man and therefore didn't think this information was all that important, but, then, why would he follow Mosiah? Only those who would hearken to the Lord followed Mosiah (Omni 1:12). This was such a major event that it was the first thing Amaleki wrote about. I propose that this is because he experienced it and his father did not. One other possibility is that Abinadom journeyed with his son to Zarahemla and then allowed Amaleki to write about the event. This still would not explain why Abinadom would expressly say that he knew of no new prophecy or revelation.

Lastly I would urge caution in some of the dating suggestions in this region. Many dates given in the Book of Mormon first appear in the 1920 edition of the Book of Mormon edited by James E. Talmage. Most are based on actual dates found in the text, but others are only estimates when no information is available. One such is the 130 B.C. date shown below the footnotes (pages 141-142) in association with the ending of the small plates and presumably the death of Amaleki. This date appears to be a best guess and not associated with any particular piece of information in the text. So Amaleki could have died many years earlier, allowing for him to be a more reasonable age at his death.

4 Jacob 1:1–8; 7:27; Jarom 1:1–2, 15; Omni 1:1.

5 It's tough to know where Zeniff enters in this era of history. What little we do know seems to indicate that he was part of the group coming out of Nephi. Years later when he chooses to return to Nephi, he describes in his own record, "I Zeniff . . . having had a knowledge of the land of Nephi (Mosiah 9:1).

6 Jacob 7:26.

7 I mentioned the significance of this hill in endnote 2, but it is worth mentioning again. The hill north of Shilom was said to be a "resort" to the people of Mosiah when they fled out of the land (Mosiah 11:13), but we also see reference to it later. Upon the Nephites' return to the land of Nephi, Noah builds a great tower there (whether as monument or military outpost it doesn't say). Also during Limhi's reign, it was upon this same hill that Ammon and his fifteen men stopped to set up camp before they ventured into the city of Nephi (Mosiah 7:5).

8 The distance from Nephi to the Zarahemla Valley is not explicitly mentioned. It is consistently described as "many days" (Mosiah 9:4; 22:13; Alma 17:9). Mosiah 24:20–25 describes the distance from the city of Helam to Zarahemla as thirteen days, and, in Mosiah 7:4, Ammon and his party of fifteen "wandered" from Zarahemla to Nephi (not knowing the "course they should travel"), and it took them forty days.

9 There is no mention of a city in the land of Zarahemla at this time. John Sorenson suggests that the settlement may have been much different than the sophisticated city it would become under the leadership of Nephite kings ("The Mulekites," *BYU Studies* 30:3).

10 Zarahemla is never identified as a king. In fact, there seems to be no king in the land. John Sorenson suggests he may have been more of a chief ("The Mulekites," *BYU Studies* 30:3).

11 Omni 1:14.

12 2 Nephi 25:10 notes that the destruction was to happen "immediately" after Lehi left Jerusalem.

13 2 Nephi 1:6.

14 2 Nephi 1:9.

15 There is no information to indicate how Zarahemla was feeling about these events except to say that he rejoiced exceedingly, "because the Lord had sent the people of Mosiah with the plates of brass which contained the record of the Jews" (Omni 1:14). This verse seems to indicate that even though Zarahemla and his people had lost their knowledge of God (Omni 1:17), by the time Amaleki recorded what happened, Zarahemla clearly acknowledged that the Lord had sent Mosiah. With that idea in mind, I wrote this as a possibility of how Zarahemla's faith may have begun.

16 Who made the stone and when did they make it are questions for which we have no answers. It seems likely that the stone was worked many years earlier, as no one then living in the land could read it or seemed to know its history. Without written records, memories can become easily lost or corrupted. Perhaps Coriantumr was brought to live among the people of Zarahemla closer to the time of the original settlement of the city of Mulek on the eastern seashore (Alma 51:26). That would certainly explain why the stone had to be "brought" (Omni 1:20) to Mosiah sometime during his reign rather than simply taking him to the large stone.

17 This is what we know about the Urim and Thummim that was possessed by the Nephites and buried with the plates of Mormon: They originated with the brother of Jared at least two thousand years before Mosiah's day (Ether 3:22–28; D&C 17:1). How they got from the Jaredites to the Nephites is not known. I am making my best guess here. It is worth noting that Mosiah's experience with the large stone is the first recorded event in the New World when someone translated unknown engravings "by the gift and power of God" (one possible exception being Aminadi in Alma 10:2). This is also exactly how Joseph Smith describes the experience of translating the plates of Mormon two thousand years later. Some wonder if the Urim and Thummim were kept with the twenty-four gold plates of Ether, but the timeline doesn't work out well. By the time the plates were discovered by the men of Limhi, Mosiah's grandson Mosiah is already said to be in possession of "interpreters" that can translate ancient writing (Mosiah 8:13).

As shown in the story, I propose that the Urim and Thummim were kept as a sacred relic by the Jaredite kings (just as the Nephite kings kept theirs). Perhaps they were a sign of the true king. But after so many generations of wickedness, it also seems possible that their sacred purpose was lost to the people. Perhaps they were just used to adorn kingly vestments. Mosiah would have recognized them for what they were.

18 Probably anywhere from two to three thousand years, depending on the source you reference.

First a man of war and then a convert to peace, he would bring his followers back to the land of their fathers.

6 zeniff
The Nephites Return to Nephi

❧ Mosiah 9–10, Omni 1:27–30 ❧

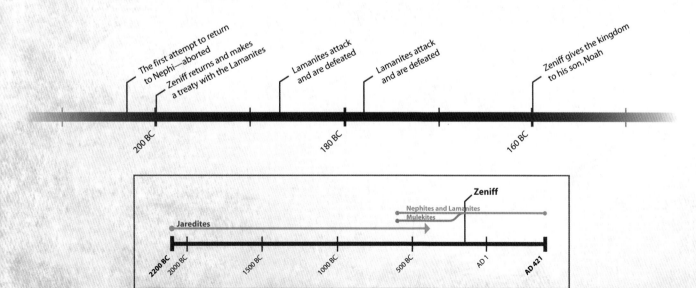

The first attempt to return to Nephi—aborted

Zeniff returns and makes a treaty with the Lamanites

Lamanites attack and are defeated

Lamanites attack and are defeated

Zeniff gives the kingdom to his son, Noah

200 BC   180 BC   160 BC

Zeniff

Nephites and Lamanites
Mulekites

Jaredites

2200 BC 2000 BC   1500 BC   1000 BC   500 BC   AD 1   AD 421

Zeniff moved through the dappled light of the forest like a ghost, quickly advancing from one patch of shadow to the next, melting into the cover of foliage. As he drew nearer to the city of Nephi,[1] he kept close to the dense underbrush and moved even more stealthily. He could not allow himself to be seen. The Lamanites could not suspect his approaching army—until it was too late.

At the sound of voices, Zeniff slipped into the cover of the underbrush, quickly removing his knife from its sheath. Beyond the next stand of trees lay a settlement, situated just outside the crumbling walls that once defended the Nephite capital.

Laughter.

Zeniff froze and watched as a small group of Lamanite children ran through the clearing in front of him, playing a racing game as they fetched water. He remained hidden, watching until they had come and gone, Then he crept closer to the village edge so he could observe further.

What he saw caught him off guard. As he had expected, the Lamanites were neither a sophisticated nor an industrious people, but Zeniff had not expected to see so much . . . love. He watched, puzzled, as fathers returned home from a hunt and mothers watched after their children with smiling faces. The children squealed in delight as they played, stopping every so often to help with a chore.

It was not uncommon for the Nephites to call the Lamanites "brethren"[2]—they were related after all—but this was the first time Zeniff felt it.

A twig snapped behind him, and Zeniff spun around to face his attacker. He relaxed almost immediately as he stared into the eyes of a small Lamanite child, who met his gaze without flinching. The boy was holding a vibrant yellow feather in his hands, extending it toward Zeniff.

The warrior reached out to accept the offering, smiling slightly so he didn't frighten the boy, although there seemed to be little threat of that happening. The child patted Zeniff's outstretched hand as if he were an old family friend.

Just then, one of the older Lamanite girls began calling for her little brother. The child turned to respond, and when he looked back, only the slight rustle of the brush indicated that Zeniff had ever been there.

❧❀❧

"How *dare* you threaten this mission!" The powerfully
built man towered over his scout, but Zeniff remained
unmoved, staring defiantly at his commander, Malik, who had stopped
just in front of him.

Malik spoke again, this time through clenched teeth, "Say no more of this, Zeniff, and you
might live to see the end of this campaign."

Zeniff watched as the men behind Malik shifted uneasily, their hands resting upon their
weapons. Sides were already clearly drawn, with some men supporting Malik and some Zeniff.

"I will say it again—there is no reason to destroy them!" Zeniff said, looking fearlessly into the eyes
of his superior. "There is much good among them. Let us enter into a treaty with the Lamanite
king.[3] Perhaps there can be peace between our people."

"There will be no *peace!*" bellowed the commander, pounding his fists through the air in
exasperation. With a low growl, he grabbed Zeniff by the tunic. "They are a scourge that must
be dealt with accordingly. We will kill every man, woman, and child among them and take back
what is ours!" He pushed Zeniff to the ground as a roar of approval went up from the men
standing behind him.

Zeniff rose to his feet. "I will not, in cold blood, slay a single one of our brethren, the Lamanites—" He scarcely had time to duck before Malik's sword sliced the air where Zeniff's head had been just moments before.

Before the commander could strike again, Zeniff raised his sword in one hand and his knife in the other. The commander stared at him with unveiled loathing. He slowly raised his arm and pointed at Zeniff.

"Kill him!"

Men from both sides rushed forward. The battle had begun.

The sun was just beginning to set when the sounds of bloody conflict finally subsided. Men lay scattered across the field of battle, the last rays of light falling over the broken bodies. Father had fought against father and brother against brother, one side arguing for war while the other fought for peace. In the end, almost the entire army had fallen.

Zeniff finally sheathed his knife and looked around, his expression grim. In the gathering darkness he could hear the occasional cough or moan coming from the men whose bodies covered the ground. A few stumbled around the battlefield, their eyes wide and staring, not fully comprehending what had happened.

One young soldier scanned the bloody ground in horror, and then staggered over to where Zeniff sat resting his head on his arms.

"What do we do now?" he asked, his voice beseeching. He stared down at his blood-covered hands as if unsure they were really his.

Zeniff looked at him for a moment. "We'll need to make a count of the survivors," he said, hanging his head wearily, unwilling to face the grim scene before him. When he glanced up a moment later, the young soldier had not moved.

"I . . . I killed my own brother," he whispered.

"You weren't the only one," Zeniff responded curtly. He sighed. "Go," he said more gently, "and make a count of the survivors."

In the end, only fifty remained of the army that once intended to take back the lands of their inheritance—only fifty to stumble back to Zarahemla and tell the wives and children the pitiable tale.

Amaleki looked in the open doorway of Zeniff's homestead and watched as his old friend gathered supplies. "So the rumors are true, then. You're going back." It was more of a statement than a question. Amaleki was disappointed but not surprised. Zeniff had been preparing for this journey for months. He had amassed a considerable number of followers who were willing to travel with him.[4]

"This time things will be different," Zeniff answered evenly as he bundled together strips of dried venison. "We are not going to war. We are going recolonize the land peacefully."

"Peacefully?" replied Amaleki with thinly veiled sarcasm. "How exactly do you propose to do that? Ask King Laman to please give our lands back?"

Zeniff sat on the bags of grain he had filled earlier and looked at Amaleki with a hopeful smile. "Don't you see? We have a chance to start over. To build a mighty nation again in the land of our fathers."

"We're starting over and building a mighty nation right here," countered Amaleki. "Why not stay and help us? The Lamanites don't even know we are here. For once we have peace!"

"I too long for peace," Zeniff replied wistfully. "I believe we *can* have peace in our homeland of Nephi. Surely you know I am not the only one who feels that way."

Amaleki sat down on Zeniff's sacks of grain, his face drawn in defeat. "I know. You have certainly won the hearts of many. Even my brother desires to go with you." The two men were silent for a time. After a few moments, Amaleki arose and began filling another grain sack. Then he turned and added, "King Benjamin is not happy about this, you know."

"I know," Zeniff replied, standing to help his friend. "He is a young king and labors under the burden of his late father's desire to keep his people united."[5]

"And safe," Amaleki amended, looking pointedly at Zeniff. "Have you considered the fact that you may only agitate our enemies and lead them to us?[6] You knowingly risk your own safety and the safety of those who follow you, but have you thought about the rest of us?"

Zeniff looked at Amaleki with compassion. "This is a mission of peace—intended to benefit all our nations."

Amaleki looked unconvinced, but he nodded.

After a moment, Zeniff changed the subject. "I have been wondering," he began, looking away for the first time, "will you write of our disastrous first journey in the small plates of Nephi?"

"There is not much room left, but I intend to mention the basics of the affair," Amaleki replied. "I'll simply say that a group left Zarahemla to reinherit the land of Nephi, that their leader caused a contention, and that all save fifty were slain."

"Could you . . . could you not say that only fifty survived?" Zeniff pleaded. He felt the horror and humiliation of that day would never leave him. "Couldn't you just say that the greater number of our army was destroyed and leave it at that?"[7]

"I will bear that in mind," replied Amaleki with a sad smile. "Perhaps I simply should not mention any names."

"That would be fine with me," Zeniff said as he threw the last of the grain sacks on the pile. Wiping the sweat from his brow, he added, "And tell your brother to come see me. I could use a man from the priestly lineage of Jacob[8]—since you refuse to come with us."

Amaleki shook his head as he clasped hands with Zeniff in a final farewell. "Since you will not listen to reason, will you at least promise to keep a record of your doings? I know you have been taught in all the language of our people."[9]

"That I will," Zeniff covenanted solemnly. And for a final time, the two friends parted.

Though their journey was filled with tribulation, Zeniff and his followers finally arrived in the land of Nephi, setting up camp on the very site that marked the disastrous end of the previous journey. Then Zeniff, accompanied by four of his men, left the others and sought an audience with the king.

King Laman was more than a bit surprised when Zeniff and his attendants marched straight into the city and petitioned for an audience with him. His astonishment only grew when he learned that a number of Nephites had survived the purge and were living in a land far to the north. Now this man, Zeniff, was requesting the lands of Lehi-Nephi so that he and his followers could once again live in the

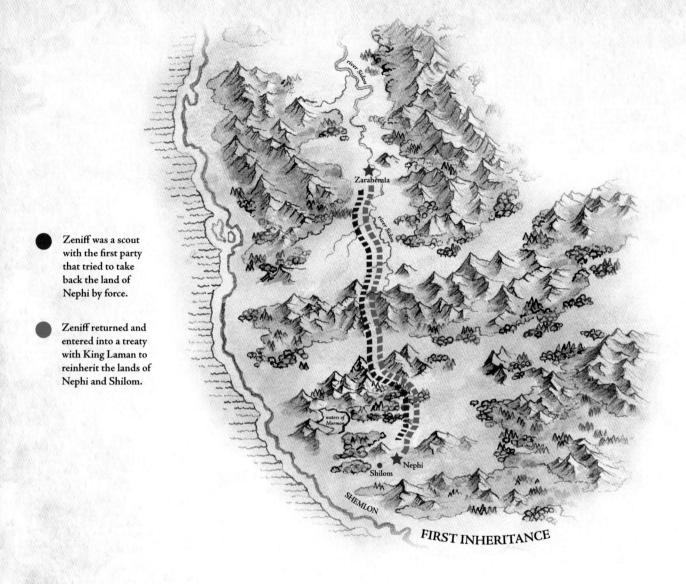

Zeniff was a scout with the first party that tried to take back the land of Nephi by force.

Zeniff returned and entered into a treaty with King Laman to reinherit the lands of Nephi and Shilom.

river Sidon

Zarahemla

river Sidon

waters of Mormon

Nephi

Shilom

SHEMLON

FIRST INHERITANCE

land of their fathers. As the king considered the request, a cunning smile curled his lips. To the shock of the entire court, he willingly made a treaty with Zeniff. The matter, however, was far from closed.

"Father, I don't understand," the king's son, Laman, being named after his father, said after Zeniff and his men had departed. The boy seemed almost angry. "Why would you give away our best cities without asking for anything in return?"

"Why indeed," echoed King Laman. "Why would we want the Nephites back in our domain?" He spoke as if the answer was so obvious that no one need take the time to explain. The prince huffed in frustration, but the king paid him no mind and turned instead to the man standing at his left.

"Captain, clear our people from the cities of Lehi-Nephi, Shilom, and their surrounding lands. Make haste, for we must prepare for our new guests."

After bowing to their king, the captain and his men turned to depart.

"Oh, and, Captain," King Laman added, "send our best hunters and trackers to follow the Nephites' trail to the north. Bring me word of what they find."

"They are sons of a thief and a liar!" the prince finally exploded then turned from his father, extending his speech to any one who would listen. "The Nephites will bring a curse upon us."

The king calmly reached out and grabbed the young man's cape, pulling him back down to his seat. "I am the king, and I want the Nephites here." He wore a bemused smile as he looked at his son's scowling face. "I want them here to repair the palace and the other grand buildings, to fortify the walls of the cities, and to build new structures. And I want crops! I want corn and wheat and barley!"

King Laman's eyes glittered with excitement as he spoke. "But that is not all, my son. I want all manner of fruits and flocks, and the Nephites can give them to me. I know these people. They will labor all the day long, and in time they will provide us with *everything* we desire. We must be patient, but the reward will be great. Anything we want, we will just . . . take."

Slowly, the prince nodded. Then he smiled. He was beginning to understand.

King Laman did indeed understand the Nephite people well—they were an industrious people. Once they moved into their new lands, they immediately began to construct buildings and repair the dilapidated walls of the city, both in Lehi-Nephi[10] and the city of Shilom. Crops of all kinds sprung up, and the people of Zeniff began to multiply and prosper in the land.

For thirteen years the people enjoyed peace and plenty, but at last the day arrived when King Laman was ready to collect his debt.

"King Zeniff! Help us!" cried a desperate voice. Zeniff ran outside and saw a man dashing toward him, followed by a haggard mob of men, women, and children. All wore the same expression of fear and grief.

The man leading the crowd collapsed at Zeniff's feet. "They came from the south . . ." he gasped. "No warning . . . numerous Lamanites . . . began to slay us . . . stole our flocks . . . raided our fields." He looked up in wild-eyed desperation, searching for a sign of comprehension in the king's eyes. "The city of Shilom is lost!"

Zeniff's eyes widened, but his shock quickly hardened into a firm resolve. Without wasting a moment, he turned to gather his people. This treachery would not go unanswered.

"Gather all the weapons you can find, or whatever weapon you can invent! Empty the armory!" Zeniff shouted, surrounded by the walls of the city of Nephi. Then he raised his hand to quiet the crowd's murmurs. Though it was vital that his people be armed, they could not rely on their strength alone.

"But this is not all, my people. Hear me well—each of you must cry mightily unto the Lord and ask Him to deliver us from our enemies." A hush fell over the crowd, and Zeniff continued. "Many of you can still remember the journey that brought us into this land. Surely you recall that we were slow to remember the Lord our God—and surely you remember the sore afflictions and famine that our slothfulness and neglect brought upon us.

"Now I would have you turn your minds to the goodness of God in delivering Mosiah and our people out of the hands of the Lamanites." Zeniff lifted his arms skyward. "He can deliver us! He will answer our cries and make us mighty against our enemies! Let us go forward now in the strength of the Lord!"

With a prayer on their lips and in their hearts, Zeniff's people armed themselves and marched against the invading army. Their prayers were answered, for God truly worked a miracle that day. When the battle was over and the enemy had been driven out of the land, three thousand forty-three slain Lamanites were left behind.

Zeniff stopped digging for a moment and sat down to rest. They had buried so many already, but bodies still covered the ground. He glanced up to see the captain of his forces limping toward him. Like the rest of his men, he was exhausted.

"What news?" the king asked wearily. "Do we have a count of our losses?"

The captain's voice was even, but his eyes seemed unable to comprehend the words his mouth spoke. "Two hundred and seventy-nine."

The king shook his head in amazement. Two hundred and seventy-nine Nephites had perished, while more than three thousand Lamanites had been slain. It was undeniably a miracle, yet Zeniff's army was composed of so few men that even this loss would be deeply felt.

As he thought of the men's wives and families, Zeniff was helpless to stop the wave of sorrow that washed over him. A single tear rolled down his face before he wiped it away and returned to the grim task of burying the dead.

Zeniff never again allowed his people to be caught off their guard now that the treachery of King Laman had been revealed. He ordered weapons of war to be made and posted guards throughout the land. Once more, the people lived in peace and prospered.

King Laman never returned after this first crushing defeat, and nine years passed before Zeniff again feared for his people's safety. When news reached him of the

Lamanite king's death and his son's ascension to the throne, Zeniff immediately sent spies down into Shemlon. They learned that the Lamanites were indeed preparing for war against them yet again.

"Are you certain you wish to do this, Father?" One of Zeniff's sons, Noah, asked, looking at him with concern. Preparations had been underway to arm all the men, young and old, who could fight. The women and children were safely hidden in the wilderness.

"You think me too old, do you?" Zeniff responded, raising an eyebrow as he prepared to inspect the ranks.

"Do not take offense, Father, but the Lamanites are a powerful people. How can we hope to match their strength?" Noah's face darkened. "And it's not just you. Many of our ranks are too old and feeble. They will be useless against our enemy. It would be better for them to flee into the wilderness with the women and children," he finished derisively.

"My son, you need not worry yourself about the strength of men," Zeniff counseled as they made their way to the front of the ranks. The king had divided the men up by age and was proud to see determination in their eyes, young and old alike.

Zeniff turned to face his warriors and raised his voice for all to hear. "You must not put your trust in the arm of flesh!" he cried, momentarily letting his gaze fall on his son. "The Lamanites are strong as to the strength of men, but they know nothing concerning the strength of the Lord! Our enemies foster an eternal hatred toward us. They believe they were wronged by our father Nephi, so they will not hesitate to destroy us from off the face of the earth."

As the warriors sent up a rallying cry, Zeniff added, "But we will put our trust in the Lord and in His might, and we will defend our lands and our families—for our God is with us!"

The Lamanites thought themselves clever for attacking Shilom from the north this time but were disappointed. Zeniff and his men were expecting them. The Nephites cut through their ranks and quickly gained the upper hand. This time so many Lamanites perished that Zeniff's army did not even number the dead.

Zeniff's life had been filled with trials and hardships, but he succeeded in overcoming all obstacles with the help of the Lord. In the final words of his personal record, he offered a benediction upon his people: "And may the Lord bless my people. Amen."

Zeniff gave his son Noah the trust of the kingdom before he died, but Noah did not walk in the ways of his father, and he introduced great wickedness among the people—but that's another story.

FIRST INHERITAN

Zeniff ◆ 77

Endnotes

1   Zeniff's account is unique in that he constantly refers to land of Nephi as "the land of our fathers" (Mosiah 9:1, 3–4; 10:3). He is the only author who does, so when he said that their army's camp was near "the land of our fathers," he must have meant the land of Nephi.

2   The word *brethren* was used to describe fellow Nephites, Lamanites, Mulekites, and even (in at least one statement) the Jaredites (Mosiah 1:5; 7:2, 13; 11:19; Alma 24:7–8 and 46:22).

3   Mosiah 9:2.

4   Omni 1:29.

5   Working out the timeline in this section was tricky at best. It is unclear who was king (Mosiah or Benjamin) when Zeniff departed out of the land, so I decided to make it both. I hint at the idea that Mosiah was aware of the failed first journey to take back the land of Nephi and that Benjamin had since become the king. By proposing Mosiah's deathbed desire that his son keep the people together, I am trying to show that perhaps there was friction between Zeniff's group and the remaining Nephites.

Friction between the groups would certainly help explain the conspicuous absence of any contact between the two Nephite groups for the next two or three generations. Even the Lamanites, when they are at peace with the Nephites, "open a correspondence" between the lands of Nephi and Zarahemla (Alma 23:18; 24:8–9; Helaman 6:8). So why would there be no communication between Zeniff's group and the rest of the Nephites?

6   It is a sad coincidence that only after Zeniff sets his people up in the land of Nephi do the Lamanites figure out where the rest of the Nephites have gone. The Lamanites sent a powerful army to destroy the Nephites in Zarahemla, and it was only with the loss of much blood that King Benjamin was able to repel them (Omni 1:24; Words of Mormon 1:13–14).

7   This is just a little humor comparing how each person actually recorded the account of Zeniff's first journey (compare Omni 1:27–28 with Mosiah 9:2).

8   Amaleki's brother does go with Zeniff (Omni 1:30). I mentioned the priestly lineage of Jacob because of the role Jacob played (2 Nephi 5:26) and because his descendants kept the religious record. This is just speculation, but if priesthood was passed down through that lineage, it would explain how the priesthood came to be among Zeniff and his people. Zeniff certainly consecrated righteous priests (Mosiah 11:5), and we know that this priesthood carried authority since Alma was able to baptize with it in the Waters of Mormon and to ordain other priests (Mosiah 18:13, 18).

9   Some feel that Zeniff's admission that he had "been taught in all the language of the Nephites" (Mosiah 9:1) means that he was not a Nephite by birth. In that same verse, however, he identifies the land of Nephi as the "land of our fathers' first inheritance."

Another explanation of the phrase "taught in all the language of the Nephites" can be seen if we look at how other writers in the Book of Mormon started their own records.
- Nephi: "I was taught somewhat in all the learning of my father" (1 Nephi 1:1).
- Enos: "He was a just man—for he taught me in his language" (Enos 1:1).
- King Benjamin caused that his sons, "should be taught in all the language of his fathers" (Mosiah 1:2).
- Mormon: "I began to be learned somewhat after the manner of the learning of my people" (Mormon 1:2).

Each writer seemed to want us to know, right up front, that they were taught specific skills that allowed them to keep the record as well as read past records. The way Moroni describes the Nephite use of language in Mormon 9:32–33 does make it sound complicated.

10 After the Lamanite occupation of the land of Nephi, the land seems to be, for a limited time at least, more commonly called the land (or city) of Lehi-Nephi. I have wondered if the original Lamanite land was called Lehi (because it was the land where Lehi first landed) and when it was joined by the Lamanite-conquered land of Nephi, the Lamanites just combined the two names. Regardless of the reason, the land is identified as Lehi-Nephi in only a handful of verses in two chapters of Mosiah (Mosiah 7:1–2, 4, 21 and 9:6, 8).

A wicked priest, murderer, kidnapper, and coward. His mistake was thinking he could escape God's curse given to him through a dying prophet.

7 Amulon
Cursed for Generations

Mosiah 11–24, Alma 25

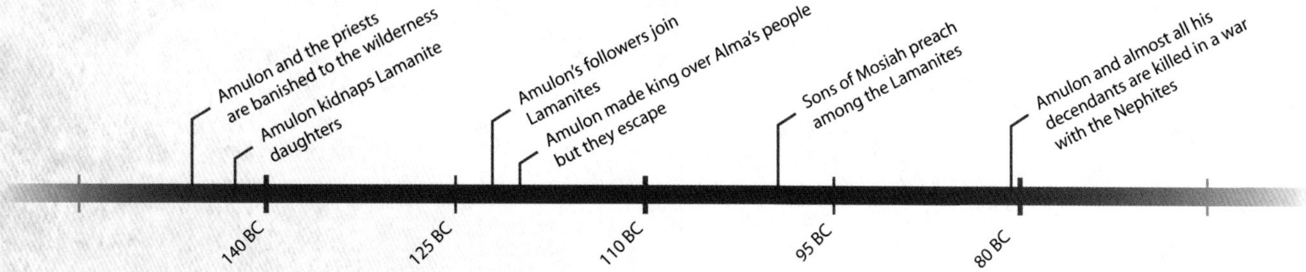

Amulon and the priests are banished to the wilderness

Amulon kidnaps Lamanite daughters

Amulon's followers join Lamanites

Amulon made king over Alma's people but they escape

Sons of Mosiah preach among the Lamanites

Amulon and almost all his decendants are killed in a war with the Nephites

140 BC — 125 BC — 110 BC — 95 BC — 80 BC

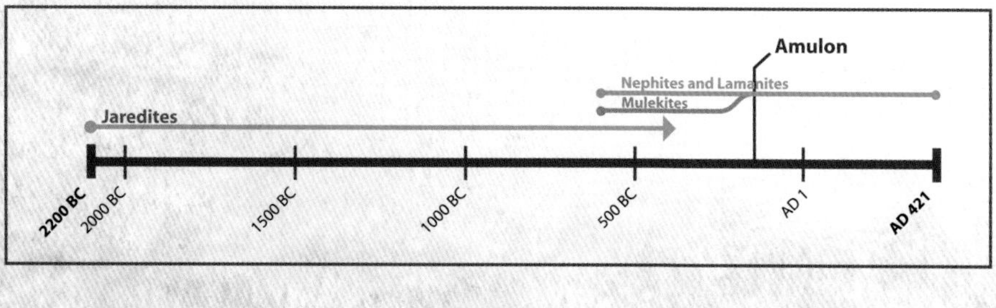

Amulon

Nephites and Lamanites
Mulekites

Jaredites

2200 BC — 2000 BC — 1500 BC — 1000 BC — 500 BC — AD 1 — AD 421

They are going to kill the king, Amulon thought with sudden surety. King Noah glanced behind him in the direction from which he and his men had just fled, oblivious to the dangerous hostility on the faces of the men surrounding him. Amulon's gaze rested upon the king, who had not yet realized that the loyalty of his men had evaporated. Under Noah's command, these men had abandoned their wives and children, leaving them to die at the hands of a bloodthirsty Lamanite army. The guilt for their cowardice was beginning to consume them.

"We have to go back!" one man cried out, his eyes wild. "I must know what has happened to my family."

"To what end?" replied the king loud enough for all to hear, his voice devoid of compassion, his tone betraying frustration at his men's anxiety. "The Lamanites have probably killed them all—my family, your family, everyone who could not keep up."

"Then we will seek revenge against our enemy!" shouted another man, raising his spear high into the air. "We may perish, but we will take some of the devils with us!"

"Don't be a fool!" Noah shouted back. "We are safe now, and I will protect you." He turned to continue forward. "Even from yourselves," he muttered. No one followed after him. Sensing he still had not gotten through to them, the king spun around and put it in the simplest of terms, "I forbid you to leave!"

The men looked at their king as if he had just struck each one of them in the face. Amulon watched them all from the side of the group. Noah had just squandered his last chance to redeem himself in the eyes of his men.

"Without me, you would all be dead now, hacked down by a murderous army," the king pushed on.

"Like our women and children, you mean?" someone called out. "Because we followed you, we left them to be butchered."

The men slowly began advancing toward Noah.

"Yes, they are dead," growled the king in frustration. "What matters now is us! Our future!"

"Future?" questioned a voice of frightening calm. One of the men approached Noah, smiling slightly and shaking his head while the other men began to encircle the king. "There is no future for you."

The men strode forward, their stony faces devoid of mercy. Noah's hastily drawn sword soon tumbled to the ground, and despite his attempts to strike the men surrounding him, they quickly had him bound. Then Amulon saw the hastily made bundles of wood. As they were lit one by one, the king commanded them to stop, then he screamed, then he begged. But the men paid him no heed and continued preparing their grim ceremony.

Amulon and the other priests kept silent through it all, hoping to somehow escape the mob's anger. But as the flames licked at the king's robes, Noah began to call to them, pleading for deliverance. The men then turned to face their next sacrifice.

Knowing there was no hope of reconciliation, Amulon and Noah's priests fled into the forest. They did not dare glance back to see if they were still being pursued. They could only run. The smell of smoke followed them, haunted them, and Noah's screams echoed in their ears. They did not stop until their legs gave out and they could run no farther.

"I do not think . . . we are being followed any longer," Himnor, one of the priests gasped, falling to his knees and leaning against a tree as he struggled to breathe. Noah's priests were accustomed to a life of luxury. That they had been able to run as far as they had astonished each one of them.

"What will we do now?" lamented Kish, another priest who had his face in his hands. "We have no supplies. We have no shelter. We are alone!" He began to weep. "Oh, Lord, our God, have mercy on us . . ."

"Silence!" Amulon shouted, raising his hand as if to strike the quivering priest. "Have you so quickly forgotten who you are? Priests! Men of power and authority. We cower before no one—especially not the God who has abandoned us!" He glared at his stunned companions. "What we need, we will take. That is the privilege of our position."

The priests turned to face him, taking courage at his words. Amulon continued. "For a time, life will be difficult. But I assure you that we will rise again—it is our destiny!"

The first night in the wilderness was the worst. Sleep came on slowly—if at all—as they lay on the uneven ground with the chill of the night air at their backs and the haunting sounds of the forest echoing in their ears. Memories of Noah's screams disturbed any dreams they had. In only a few short hours they had been deprived of their riches, comfortable homes, food, servants, women, and children. Even their nation was lost to them now.

Amulon remained awake, thoughts of revenge swirling in his mind. His bitter musings finally rested on Alma, a former priest who had rebelled against them. Alma had stirred up the people, making them question the priests' authority. Then he had led his followers into the wilderness, teaching them the words of *Abinadi*. Amulon whispered the name, gritting his teeth in disdain. Abinadi was never far from his thoughts, but tonight he could think of nothing else. Amulon and his fellow priests had demanded the fiery death of that so-called prophet, and tonight Abinadi's final words played over and over in the chief priest's mind, tormenting him as he tried, in vain, to sleep.

"Behold, even as ye have done unto me, so shall it come to pass that thy seed shall cause that many shall suffer the pains that I do suffer, even the pains of death by fire; and this because they believe in the salvation of the Lord their God. And it will come to pass that ye shall be afflicted with all manner of diseases because of your iniquities. Yea, and ye shall be smitten on every hand, and shall be driven and scattered to and fro, even as a wild flock is driven by wild and ferocious beasts. And in that day ye shall be hunted, and ye shall be taken by the hand of your enemies, and then ye shall suffer, as I suffer, the pains of death by fire."

Amulon shook his head violently, as if to somehow scatter the loathsome words.

Afflicted with all manner of diseases . . . Smitten on every hand . . . Driven and scattered to and fro . . .

He gasped for breath, trying to think of something else—anything else.

Ye shall be hunted . . .

And then ye shall suffer . . . death by fire.

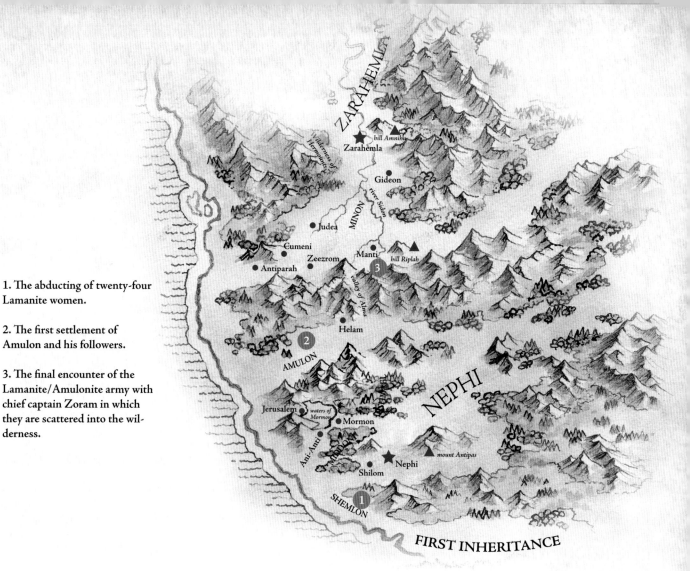

1. The abducting of twenty-four Lamanite women.

2. The first settlement of Amulon and his followers.

3. The final encounter of the Lamanite/Amulonite army with chief captain Zoram in which they are scattered into the wilderness.

laughed derisively. "But what has happened? Have we been hunted and driven? No! Look at me. *I am your king!*"

"God has power to fulfill all his words, and He will not be mocked." Alma looked Amulon straight in the eye. His voice remained impassive, as if he were the one in control of this situation. "There is no peace for the wicked. We, those who love Him, carry our peace with us no matter our circumstance."

The façade of pleasantries now over, Amulon's eyes took on a murderous sheen. "Fool! Can you not see that your God has abandoned you? I have dreamed of the moment when I would make you pay for your rebellion. Each day you live under my rule I will make absolutely certain you understand how much I loathe you for what you did, for teaching the words of the liar Abinadi and undermining your own brotherhood." He leaned closer to Alma, his hands curled in tight fists. "I blame you for every hardship and every depravity I have suffered since you left, and now you will feel the pains I have endured. I will see to that . . . personally."

to save this people? As a grizzly scene opened before her, she pushed the thoughts aside. She would not be afraid anymore. Glancing behind her, she was amazed to see the number of young women who had followed her—who were depending on her—along with those who stood behind them. She saw men with grim and hopeless faces, women crying and clutching infants close to them, small children horrified beyond reason, and elderly grandparents unable to move any farther. They would all die, every one of them, if she did not stand forth.

Mariah turned and got her first clear view of their enemy. She stared in horror at the Lamanites with their shaved heads and bare skin covered in blood. They looked more like wild animals than men—and they were coming straight toward her. She watched them hacking away with their weapons, heard the sound of crunching bones and mangled flesh, and listened to the ever-present screaming.

A wealthy maiden stood next to her and looked as though she might faint. As the girl's knees began to buckle, Mariah reached out and placed a steadying arm around her, supporting the girl with what little strength she had left. When the maiden pulled her eyes from the horror in front of her to look at Mariah, her eyes filled with recognition and then tears. She had been the one mocking Mariah in the market only a few days earlier. Mariah only held her tighter. They were no longer divided by class—they were sisters.

Mariah looked to either side, and her eyes widened as she saw a line of young women standing together, facing the oncoming menace. Many were crying, all were clearly terror-stricken, but none moved. Then the tears finally came flooding down her cheeks. Abinadi was right. The judgments of God *had* come upon this people for all their wickedness and cruelty. The king had left them to die, and a bloodthirsty army stood ready to butcher them all. But as she stood forth with these young women, she felt a strength she had never known before. She knew that she would do what must be done—give her life to save those she loved.

With a start, Mariah realized the screaming had stopped. She looked ahead at the savage warriors of the Lamanite army—yet they did not advance. Blood dripped from their weapons, and corpses littered the ground in front of them, but the Lamanites simply stared at the young women before them, their expressions filled with confusion and astonishment.

"Please," Mariah said, breaking the silence. "Have compassion upon us and our families. Let us live." Her voice was steady and overwhelmingly sincere. As her plea was repeated by other young women, the Lamanites began to lower their weapons of war.

For Mariah, the rest of the day floated in front of her like a dream. Limhi, one of King Noah's sons, was among those who had disobeyed his father's command and stayed behind. He and Gideon negotiated the surrender and terms of their bondage.[6] He also made an oath that the Nephites would pay a heavy tribute to their captors, ensuring that their lives would be difficult. But they were alive and allowed to return to their homes in the city of Nephi.

Mariah's father wrapped an arm around his daughter as they headed toward their home. He had not said a word, but the solemn gratitude in his eyes warmed her heart. For now, he simply held her tightly.

For the Nephites that remained, life would never be the same. Mariah would see a gradual but steady change come over the people. Their time in bondage to the Lamanites would prepare them to hear the words of God when they were preached again.[7] And it would all come to pass through the most unexpected of visitors—but that's another story.

Endnotes

1 Although this is one of my favorite stories, it is difficult to retell in this kind of a format. To really appreciate these events, one needs to see them through the lens of a character who is experiencing them firsthand. Unfortunately, that required developing a fictional main character, which was not my aim in telling these stories. After many attempts, this story is the final result.

2 Abinadi's ministry and death can be found in Mosiah 11:20–17:20.

3 Gideon is a mysterious man in that we don't know much about him before he is made the captain of Limhi's men. We do have some clues to help us understand his relationship to King Noah.

- Gideon is associated with a group of men who are threatening the king. This happens right after King Noah sends his military to destroy Alma and other converts (Mosiah 18:32–35; 19:2–4). I wonder what effect Noah's order had on the mood of his people (including the small military) toward him. It's one thing to attack your enemies, but attacking a peaceful religious group within your own people is pretty harsh.
- How could Gideon have had such easy access to fight with the king (Mosiah 19:5)? It doesn't seem like just anyone could pull a weapon and challenge him to a duel. Where were the king's guards during all this? This has led some to speculate that Gideon was a military leader of some sort—which would give him relatively easy access to the king and power over the guards.
- After the events described in this story, Gideon sent men to find King Noah (Mosiah 19:18). He seemed quite at home commanding men, and they obeyed. These men were even called "the men of Gideon" (Mosiah 19:22).
- The group of men who fled with King Noah then killed him and returned to Nephi reported directly to Gideon (Mosiah 19:24).
- By Mosiah 20:17, Gideon is clearly identified as King Limhi's captain. Could this be because he was a captain (or some other military leader) under the reign of King Noah?

4 Mosiah 11:19.

5 The account of these events in Mosiah 19:9–14 is so brief that it makes it hard to imagine how they might have unfolded. For example, it never says how everyone made the decision to have the "fair daughters" stand forth. It makes sense that a leader would stand up and pull the people together, and I could think of no one better for this role than Gideon.

6 The scriptural account doesn't specifically state that Gideon and Limhi negotiated the surrender, but who else would do it? Gideon and Limhi seem to be working together as early as Mosiah 19:17–18.

7 Another exciting element of this story is that it demonstrates the first time these people had ever done anything truly selfless. Under the reign of King Noah, the people were supported in committing "all manner of wickedness" (Mosiah 11:2). Abinadi started a spiritual revolution, which was carried on by Alma. But after Alma and his converts departed to safer lands, who was left? Only the prideful who would not follow.

When told to save themselves, almost all of the men eventually chose to die with their families (Mosiah 19:12, 19). Their fair daughters stood forth, as described here, at great personal risk, to protect those they loved. These events foreshadowed a change of heart that would gradually happen over time until they were rescued and given the opportunity to enter into a covenant with God and be baptized by the very man (Alma) that they had previously rejected (Mosiah 25: 15–18).

In the crumbling ruins of a lost civilization, a team of desperate explorers found the treasure of a lifetime.

9 Limhi's Forty-Three Men The Discovery of Desolation

❯❯ *Mosiah 8, 21* ❮❮

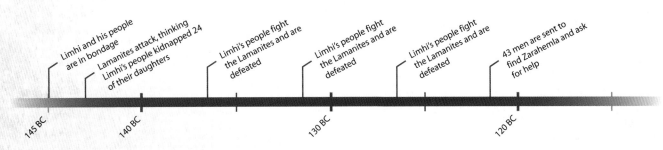

Limhi and his people are in bondage

Lamanites attack, thinking Limhi's people kidnapped 24 of their daughters

Limhi's people fight the Lamanites and are defeated

Limhi's people fight the Lamanites and are defeated

Limhi's people fight the Lamanites and are defeated

43 men are sent to find Zarahemla and ask for help

145 BC   140 BC   130 BC   120 BC

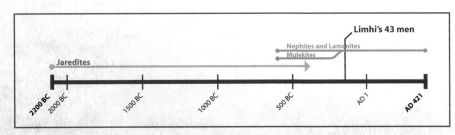

Limhi's 43 men

Nephites and Lamanites
Mulekites

Jaredites

2200 BC 2000 BC   1500 BC   1000 BC   500 BC   AD 1   AD 421

King Limhi sat alone in the throne room of the grand palace that was built by his father. With one hand he slowly stroked the polished wood of the intricately carved seat, running his fingers over the fine workmanship and ornamentation of gold, silver, and other precious things. But when he looked up, his eyes were vacant—heavy with sorrow and grief. The spacious room brimmed with elegant construction and décor in stone, wood, and precious metals,[1] but there was no real beauty here—not anymore. His people were dying. The glory of this kingdom had come to an end, and they had no one to blame but themselves.

"King Limhi!"

Absorbed by his grief,[2] the young monarch barely looked up at the summons. The king's captain strode into the room. Gideon[3] was a man of strength and wisdom. His expression was grave as he studied the despondent king for a moment and then said, "We cannot allow this people to go to war again. This is the third time they have returned beaten and bloodied. We barely have an army left to fight at all!"

The king scarcely reacted, and, when he finally spoke, his voice echoed the hopelessness shared by his people. "Shall we then fully subject ourselves to the yoke of bondage? Shall we submit to being smitten and driven to and fro? Must we endure the heavy burdens laid on our backs by our enemies?"[4]

"Yea, my lord," Gideon said plainly. When his response was met with silence, Gideon tried again. "Are not the words of the prophet Abinadi fulfilled, which he prophesied against us—and all this because we would not hearken unto the words of the Lord and turn from our iniquities?"[5]

Limhi winced slightly. Abinadi had given his life in testimony of his words. Limhi's own father had murdered him—and then Noah was in turn killed by his own subjects. Limhi had inherited his father's throne, but his people had fallen into bondage, a condemnation for their wickedness that they had been unable to escape.

"Is there nothing that can be done?" Limhi asked quietly.

Gideon stepped forward and placed his hand on the young king's shoulder in a fatherly gesture. "It is only by humbling ourselves in the depths of humility and crying mightily to our God all the day long that we can hope to be delivered from our afflictions."[6]

For the first time, the king met Gideon's gaze. When he saw he had the king's attention, Gideon continued.

"I propose that you send a small group of men into the wilderness . . . to find Zarahemla."[7]

Limhi's eyes opened wide as he absorbed Gideon's meaning. "The land my grandfather came from?"[8]

Gideon nodded. "Let us find this land and plead with our brethren that they might help us." King Limhi smiled at his captain's confidence. He had always relied on Gideon's counsel in the past, and he would continue to do so now.

"Choose your men, Gideon, and I shall see that their supplies are prepared." King Limhi arose and crossed the room with renewed purpose. "Then I shall address my people. We will do our part, and we will trust in God for the rest."

Forty-three men were chosen and outfitted for their mission. Their instructions were vague at best, since no one had traveled to Zarahemla since Limhi's grandfather. The search party was to travel northward through the wilderness and down into the great Sidon River Valley. Limhi believed that the River Sidon would lead them to Zarahemla.[9] Each of the forty-three men knew this journey would be rife with danger and difficulty, but each man also knew what was at stake.

Laden with supplies and the good wishes of all those they left behind, they began their journey northward through a tangle of wilderness. With each passing day, they expected to find the great river that would lead them to their destination, but they were disappointed. They ventured onward, keeping to their northward course across the rough terrain. Though their supplies were dwindling rapidly, the diligent travelers pressed on.

After many days of rigorous trekking with no sign of the landmark they sought, the men finally accepted the inevitable conclusion—they were lost.[10] Yet there was no choice but to continue onward, until either their supplies or strength were utterly wasted.

"Captain!" An excited voice broke through the stillness of the predawn morning, raising more than one protest from the weary company. Esrom, the youngest member of the party, raced into camp, calling for everyone's attention. "Captain! Everyone! Come quickly! I've never seen anything like it!" No one moved. Esrom looked around. The men were tired and slow to respond. He looked to their captain, Ramnah, and pointed toward the rocky hill behind him. "You need to see this."

Ramnah couldn't fathom what the boy was so anxious about, but he did not want ruin his excitement. Enthusiasm was rare at this stage of their journey. He stood to follow, and the other men reluctantly rose as well. The group had stopped for the night at the base of this steep hill, intending to travel around it the next day. To their surprise, Esrom began ascending the rocky side.

"Come on!" he cried, and the others slowly climbed after him.

As a gentle glow began to brighten the eastern horizon, the captain's thoughts drew into clearer focus. He knew it was unlikely and perhaps even foolish to hope, but could it be the city? Could Esrom have found Zarahemla? Ramnah quickened his pace, grabbing on to root and rock, eager now to reach the top.

As the group moved farther up the steep slope, the captain began to notice strange formations in the rocks. Some looked remarkably like serpents or the faces of men weathered into the stone. He then stopped short and stared as a haunting sight loomed in the predawn light. A gaping doorway seemed to have been cut into the hill, and lying across its threshold were bones—human bones.

The sun burst forth from the east and soft light flooded the scene before them. A collective gasp rose from the travelers. There was no longer any doubt that they were standing on what had once been a grand structure. Before them stretched a deserted land, covered with ruins of every kind of building.

They stood in silence for a few moments, surveying their surroundings. The landscape revealed sparse, large trees among lower-lying shrubs and vegetation.[11] The buildings that dotted the landscape were crumbling, and everywhere the travelers looked they saw the bones of men and beasts. Finally, Ramnah whispered what all were surely thinking.

"Zarahemla . . ."

Esrom, who had worn a smile throughout their trek up the hillside, turned to look back at him. Horror lit upon his face as the captain's meaning sunk in. Zarahemla had been destroyed. No one would be coming to deliver them. Several of the men collapsed against the wall behind them, exhausted and fearful of what their discovery would mean to their families in the land of Nephi. Zarahemla had been destroyed, and no one would be coming to help them.

The party spent several days surveying the ruins. They quickly concluded that this city had been the scene of a horrific battle. Along with the bones, they found many rusted swords and large breastplates made of copper and brass. Ramnah looked over the city, overrun with leafy plants and vines, and he tried to imagine what it was like in its full glory. *It must have been incredible*, he thought sadly as he turned toward his men, indicating that they should prepare to leave.

The party was fortunate enough to find water and other supplies nearby for their journey home. Sources of water abounded here—rivers, streams, ponds, and reservoirs. There were also numerous cultivated plants and trees, which, though overgrown with no one to tend them, still bore some fruit.[12] They also packed up breastplates and swords as a witness for their people of the sad story they would tell.

As he was about to call his men together, Ramnah noticed that Esrom was carefully scaling the ruins of what must have once been a grand building. When he reached a gaping hole in the

dilapidated roof, a strange look crossed his face. He looked down at the captain and motioned for the others to come up as well.

Ramnah and several other men hurried to join Esrom. Once they had reached him, he quickly ushered them inside the crumbling edifice.

A beam of light from the opening in the ceiling shone down upon a weathered stone box, its lid cracked and partially broken open by falling debris.[13] As Ramnah stepped forward, he saw what had caught Esrom's attention. There, beneath the cracked lid, an object glittered in the rays of sunlight. The captain knelt by the box and removed a heavy metal book. He gently leafed through each of the twenty-four golden plates.

"What does it say?" Esrom whispered reverently, reaching out to touch the engraved letters.

"I don't know," Ramnah replied. "It's some language I've never seen before. A record, perhaps?"

The captain tucked the record carefully in his pack, hoping that someone would be able to read the engravings on the plates and discover what had happened to these people. He looked up at his men with a brief nod. "Let's go home."

When the search party finally returned to the land of Nephi, they shared their sad news with the king. *Zarahemla is laid to waste in the north country.* Their words haunted King Limhi. No one would be coming to help deliver them. He looked over the gold plates, the rusted swords, and the battle-worn breastplates. Then he put his head in his hands and wept. *How much longer will my people suffer in bondage?* Limhi prayed. *Dear Lord, when wilt Thou answer our plea for deliverance?*

The king's forty-three valiant men had made a mistake. The land they had discovered lay to the north of Zarahemla and had belonged to an ancient civilization known as the Jaredites. The record the search party had discovered would reveal the secret of who they were and what had befallen them, but there was only one man alive who could translate the language of the plates. His name was Mosiah. He was the son of Benjamin and king of Zarahemla.

Within days of the weary travelers' return, the prayers of King Limhi and his people would at last be answered. Emissaries from Zarahemla were en route to the land of Nephi at that very moment. These men from Zarahemla would set into motion a daring plan to help rescue Limhi's people from bondage—but that's another story.

Endnotes

1 Mosiah 11:8–11 describes some of the elaborate construction and remodeling projects initiated by Limhi's father, King Noah. The improvements were so grand that they would eventually be envied by the Lamanite kings, who would move their capital from Shemlon to the city of Nephi after the Nephites escaped (Mosiah 9:6–7; 10:7; 19:6; 28:1; Alma 22:1).

2 Mosiah 8:7.

3 Mosiah 19:4; 20:17–22.

4 Mosiah 21:3, 13.

5 Mosiah 20:21—Gideon originally said this after the first battle of King Limhi's reign, when the Nephites were wrongly accused of stealing twenty-four of the Lamanite daughters, but I thought it was worth repeating.

6 Mosiah 21:14, 15.

7 There is no indication in the scriptures that Gideon was the one to suggest this plan, but he often took charge and gave wise counsel (Mosiah 19:4–6, 18; 20:17–22; 22:3–9), so it seemed like the kind of thing he would say.

8 Limhi's grandfather, Zeniff, had a great desire to inherit the lands of his fathers. It seems most likely, from what few scriptures we have on the subject, that Zeniff originally came from Nephi, then traveled to Zarahemla, and then back to Nephi to reinherit the land. Omni 1:27 mentions that Zeniff's group was returning to Nephi, and in Mosiah 9:1 Zeniff tells us that he had a knowledge of the land of Nephi. Similar phrases, when used elsewhere in the scriptures, show evidence of firsthand experience rather than of just being taught something by someone else. (In 1 Nephi 1:1, Nephi described himself as "Having had a great knowledge of the goodness and the mysteries of God," speaking of the experiences of his life. Helaman 2:6 says Helaman's servant obtained a knowledge of the plans of the Gadiantons by spying among them.)

9 Scriptural accounts are actually silent on what instructions the forty-three explorers were given.

10 The men of Limhi shouldn't have felt too bad about getting lost in the Lamanite wilderness. The Lamanites themselves got lost in it after journeying only two days from the city of Nephi (Mosiah 22:16)—and they were tracking a large group of people!

11 We are not exactly sure what this land would have looked like, but it was only "desolate" in that parts of the land lacked trees large enough to be used for timber. That was the only reason. Certain areas had timber, and other areas were described as having large bodies of water and rivers. Even if timber was absent or minimal in some areas of the land of Desolation, I think there is a case for lots of shrubs, palms, and other plants (Helaman 3:4–6).

12 I pondered on what the land of Desolation must have been like originally and what would have happened to its agriculture over time. As a youth, I used to love hiking into abandoned farmsteads and finding apple or pear trees still bearing fruit while the old wooden buildings crumbled around them. I thought that might apply here.

13 The problem here was figuring out how Ether had hidden the plates. All we know from the scriptural text is found in Ether 15:33: "And he hid them in a manner that the people of Limhi did find them." So Ether hid them and Limhi's men found them. I thought about where I might hide a precious record. What if I could hide it anywhere? The entire nation had been destroyed, so Ether could go into any building, anywhere in the land. I would hide it in a prominent building, one that was very well constructed and would attract future explorers. But I wouldn't leave it out in the open for anyone to walk off with. So I would find a stone box—these were not uncommon in ancient America— and cover it up. There it would remain safe and hidden. Perhaps Ether thought the same way.

Even still, a hidden record would be impossible to find without divine help. For example, imagine your closest metropolitan city. Then imagine someone telling you to find their journal, which is hidden somewhere in the city limits, and you have only a matter of days to do it.

When the Lord is ready to reveal the record's location to the men of Limhi, how, in my version of this story, is it found? What if the building it is hidden in starts crumbling around it? What if part of the ceiling collapses, and the debris breaks open part of the stone box, revealing its glittering contents to the rays of the sun shining through the opening in the roof? This would attract the attention of the explorers, and—you know the story.

H elp seemed impossible until the
Lord answered the prayers of a desperate
people when four strangers walked out
of the wilderness.

10 Ammon and Gideon
The Deliverers of the Nephites

※ *Mosiah 20–22* ※

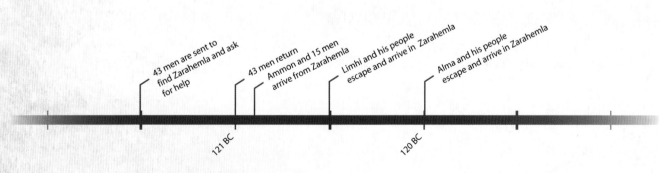

43 men are sent to
find Zarahemla and ask
for help

43 men return

Ammon and 15 men
arrive from Zarahemla

Limhi and his people
escape and arrive in Zarahemla

Alma and his people
escape and arrive in Zarahemla

121 BC

120 BC

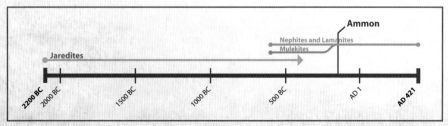

Ammon

Nephites and Lamanites
Mulekites

Jaredites

2200 BC 2000 BC   1500 BC   1000 BC   500 BC   AD 1   AD 421

Gideon strode up to the prison cell, ordering the guards to move aside with a wave of his hand. He unbolted the heavy door and pushed it open, letting light stream into the small room. Four men sat on the floor, blinking up at him. They had clearly been in the wilderness for many days, yet they looked up at him with a quiet dignity. Gideon hardly needed a glance to know that the guards had been wrong.

"These are not priests of Noah," Gideon stated, and though his gaze remained fixed on the prisoners, he could sense the guards' disappointment. "So," he said, looking down at them. "Who are you?"[1]

Gideon crossed the throne room in several great strides. "King Limhi," he called out, not caring that he was interrupting an update from one of the king's advisors. The advisor looked up, annoyed—until he saw who was speaking. When Limhi saw the expression on Gideon's face, he dismissed his advisor immediately and turned his full attention to the captain.

"My lord, I believe we would be wise to listen to what your new prisoners have to say."

Limhi's expression darkened. "My father's priests? I have heard enough of their lies to last a lifetime."

"These are not priests of Noah," Gideon responded evenly.

Limhi's eyes widened. "Who are they, then?"

"With your permission, I suggest we allow them to tell their story," Gideon replied.

After a moment's hesitation, the king nodded, and Gideon gestured toward the guards, who brought the four men into the throne room to stand before the king.

Limhi looked the men over and nodded his head, keeping his eyes trained on the prisoners. "It is as you say, Gideon."

"Remove their bindings." Gideon ordered. The prisoners were freed and commanded to stand before the king. Limhi's eyes narrowed in suspicion.

"I am Limhi, the son of Noah, who was the son of Zeniff, who came up out of the land of Zarahemla to inherit this land. And now, I desire to know the cause whereby ye were so bold as to come near the walls of the city, when I, myself, was with my guards outside the gate? And now, for this cause I have kept you alive, or else I should have caused that my guards should have put you to death."

Gideon watched surprise register on the prisoners' faces at the king's declaration. They had no way of knowing the burden Limhi's people currently endured living in bondage to the Lamanites—or the effect that daily stress had on the young king. The prisoner nearest the king, a large and muscular man, looked toward Gideon as if inquiring what action would be appropriate in this situation. The prisoners had clearly breached proper etiquette by approaching the king two days before—and they had almost lost their lives for it. They did not wish to make another mistake here.

Before Gideon could intervene, the king, sensing the prisoner's hesitancy, instructed more civilly, "You are permitted to speak."

The large man walked forward a few steps and bowed himself before the king. Then, rising again, he said, "O king, I am very thankful before God this day that I am yet alive, and am permitted

to speak; and I will endeavor to speak with boldness. I am assured that if ye had known me ye would not have suffered that I should have worn these bands. For I am Ammon, a descendant of Zarahemla, and have come up out of the land of Zarahemla to inquire concerning our brethren, whom Zeniff brought up out of that land."

Limhi's eyes widened. His team of forty-three men had only just returned from searching for the very same city. Their report was that Zarahemla had been destroyed and all its inhabitants slain in a battle long ago. Never had the king been happier to be misinformed, for he was certain that the man standing before him—Ammon—had spoken truly. A smile spread across his face, reaching his eyes for the first time in many months.

"Now, I know of a surety that my brethren who were in the land of Zarahemla are yet alive. And now, I will rejoice!" he declared.

Limhi quickly glanced out the window and, seeing that the afternoon sun was low in the sky, added, "And tomorrow I will cause that my people shall rejoice also. For behold, we are in bondage to the Lamanites, and are taxed with a tax which is grievous to be borne. And now, behold," the king said, looking at Ammon and his men with eager eyes, "our brethren will deliver us out of our bondage."

Limhi left his seat and came forward to grasp Ammon's hand "And who are these that are with you?" he asked.

"These, my good brethren, are Amaleki, Helem, and Hem," Ammon replied, and each man stepped forward at his name.

"Surely this is not all of your party. Are there more of you?" Limhi asked. He'd now transformed into the most gracious of hosts.

"There are twelve more at our camp on a hill northwest of here. We have traveled for forty days and suffered much," Ammon began.

"Say no more," Limhi said kindly, raising his hand. "You are welcome among us. Go and bring your brethren into the city, and we will prepare you a feast. You shall have food and drink, and shall rest yourselves from the labors of your journey." So great was King Limhi's joy that he stepped forward and embraced each man, a few tears of gratitude streaming down his face. He had prayed for this day for so long, and God had granted his appeal. Tomorrow all his people would know that the day of their deliverance was at hand!

The following day, word of the visitors spread quickly, and the people speculated and spoke excitedly among themselves, anxious to hear the king's announcement. Finally, when they had all been gathered at the temple, King Limhi addressed them.

"O ye, my people, lift up your heads and be comforted; for behold, the time is at hand, when we shall no longer be in subjection to our enemies. Therefore, lift up your heads, and rejoice, and put your trust in God, that same God who has brought our fathers out of the land of Jerusalem, and has kept and preserved his people even until now; and behold, it is because of our iniquities and abominations that he has brought us into bondage.

"But if ye will turn to the Lord with full purpose of heart, and put your trust in him, and serve him with all diligence of mind, if ye do this, he will, according to his own will and pleasure, deliver you out of bondage."

Shouts of joy rose in response, but they were quickly hushed as Ammon stood forth to share all that had happened in Zarahemla since the time Zeniff had left the land. Ammon also took time to share and expound upon the great words of King Benjamin's farewell speech, in which he had laid out the doctrine for those wishing to enter into a covenant with God and take His name upon them.

Ammon could see that Limhi's people had humbled themselves during the many months of bondage they had suffered. Many cheeks were wet with tears as the people listened to his message with rapt attention.

Once the king and Ammon had finished their address and dismissed the crowd, Limhi turned to his new friend, visibly touched by the events of the day and the doctrines that had been taught. "Come," he invited. "I have something else to share with you."

When they arrived at the palace, Limhi ordered that the plates containing the records of his people should be brought to him. He left Ammon and his brethren to read the account of the wickedness in the days of King Noah, the death of God's prophet, and Alma's departure from the land. It was evening before Limhi returned to check on his guests.

"We have prepared a great feast for you. Will you not come and dine with us?" Limhi asked. When they turned toward him, Limhi saw a deep sadness etched on the faces of all sixteen men from Zarahemla. "My brethren," Limhi asked quietly. "What troubles you?"

The room was silent for a few moments, everyone lost in their own thoughts but hesitant to say them aloud. Ammon finally spoke first. "So many have been slain in battle after battle. It is painful to read of the wickedness caused by your father and his abominable priests." He sighed. "So much wasted to sin."

"And a prophet of God killed," Hem added in an incredulous whisper.

The silence returned. Limhi found himself touched by how deeply these men cared about his people and their history.

"It saddens me that there is not more written about the priest Alma," Ammon said wistfully. He sat forward and put his arms on his knees, looking directly at the king. "I have not made a secret of the fact that my brethren and I have all entered into a covenant with God to serve Him and keep His commandments. To read of Alma exercising such great faith on the words of the prophet Abinadi and forming a church through the strength and power of God . . ."

Limhi watched as tears welled up in the eyes of this strong and mighty man.

"We only wish you knew where Alma and his people were now," Amaleki finished for his leader. "We would gladly join ourselves with them."

A brief movement to his side caught Limhi's attention, and he looked up to see Gideon, his fearless captain, discretely wiping at his eyes.

"As would I," Gideon said, his voice breaking slightly. He addressed Limhi as well as Ammon and his men. "I believe the words of Abinadi, which he spoke against us. I believe his teachings regarding the coming of Christ." He glanced at Ammon. "I heard those same words when you spoke today, expounding on the teachings of your late king, and they filled my heart . . ."

Gideon quieted, and Limhi felt a powerful stirring within his own soul. He felt impressed to send his servant to bring another record. When it arrived, he laid it before Ammon.

Ammon looked at the record for a moment, his brow creased in concentration. Finally he shook his head and said, "I cannot read this record. What manner of writing is this?"

King Limhi seated himself across from Ammon and told the story of the forty-three men he had sent to find Zarahemla. "After they had wandered in the wilderness, they came upon a land that had once been filled with a great many people—but it is now covered with their bones." He pointed to the record resting in front of him. "My men brought back this record. I hoped it would shed light on their sad destruction, but no one can read the writing. I hoped that perhaps . . . you might know of someone who could translate these words."

Ammon looked up, and Limhi was delighted to see a smile brightening his expression. "I can assuredly tell thee, O king, of a seer who can translate the records," Ammon began. "He possesses instruments whereby he can look and translate all records of ancient date. They are called interpreters, and they are a gift from God."

"And who is this seer?" Limhi asked in a hushed voice. "Is he a man of Zarahemla?"

"Indeed my lord," Ammon said with a smile. "He is our king. Mosiah is his name."

The two men continued to talk long into the night about prophets, seers, revelations, and hidden things brought to light by the power of God. When Limhi finally retired to his bed in the early morning hours, the joyful words he spoke before bidding good night to Ammon and his brethren echoed in mind. *How marvelous are the works of the Lord!*

"I wish to be baptized!" Limhi exclaimed as he entered the room where Ammon and his brethren slept. He was accompanied by Gideon and several of his counselors. The king had hardly slept all that night, and though he was sorry to wake Ammon so early, he could wait no longer. Limhi paced the floor as Ammon arose. "I greatly desire to enter into a covenant and serve God with all my heart," Limhi said solemnly. "And not only myself, but also my captain, Gideon, and many of my people," he added.

Ammon stared at the king. Limhi looked to have so much joy and energy that he could hardly sit still. Ammon knew he should have been overjoyed at Limhi's declaration, but he simply sat still and did not answer. In the silence that followed Limhi slowed his steps, finally stopping to look at Ammon. Something was wrong. He spoke slower now, afraid he might be guilty of a misunderstanding. "I would not venture so bold a request except that as we spoke last night I understood you had been given the authority to perform such an ordinance. Is this not true?"

"Yes, that is true," Ammon replied hesitantly, but his expression was burdened. He lowered his head and added in a quieter tone, "But I am not worthy to do so."[2]

The king's face fell. "I would not think it right for me to baptize a king and his people," Ammon said clumsily.

Gideon turned toward Limhi. "Could you not perform this ordinance in your authority as king?" he asked.

Limhi sat down and shook his head firmly. "I have no authority. I was chosen to be king by the voice of the people. Those with the proper authority are gone now—I was never consecrated as my fathers were. I will not offend God and take this honor unto myself."

"You show great wisdom," Ammon complimented, sitting beside the king. "Though I cannot help you in this respect, let us devote all our study to delivering you and your people from bondage—then all the blessings of the gospel which you desire will be granted."

"O king," Gideon said, glancing between Ammon and Limhi as he stepped forward. "If thou hast listened to my words in the past, and they have been of service to thee, please hear me now, and I will be thy servant and deliver this people out of bondage."

"Go on," said Limhi with interest.

"Behold the back pass, through the back wall, on the back side of the city. The guards of the Lamanites, by night are drunken; therefore let us send a proclamation among all this people that they gather together their flocks and herds, that they may drive them into the wilderness by night. And I will go according to thy command and pay the last tribute of wine to the Lamanites, and they will be drunken."

"And we will then slay the guards?" one of the king's counselors asked.

Gideon looked toward Ammon again. The man he once was would not have hesitated to slay the guards. But that was before—before he'd heard Abinadi prophesy, before he'd been taught by Ammon and his brethren, before he knew God.

"We will trust in God to deliver us," Gideon said meaningfully. "We will travel through the secret pass on the left of their camp when they are drunken and asleep. God willing, we'll have no need to harm them."

The plan was executed flawlessly. The people gathered their flocks, herds, and provisions in addition to what gold and other precious possessions they could carry. Though Ammon had assured Limhi's people that the king of Zarahemla would be filled with joy to receive them, Limhi insisted that it wouldn't hurt to be prepared with a peace offering for their new ruler.

The map shows:

Zarahemla

river Sidon

valley of Alma

Helam

AMULON

waters of Mormon

Mormon

Nephi

Shilom

SHEMLON

FIRST

The people traveled along the borders of the land of Shilom, following the path that Ammon and his brethren had taken not long before. After many days, they found themselves walking into the city of Zarahemla.

"King Limhi, I welcome you and your people most warmly." Mosiah, king of Zarahemla, advanced briskly to meet Limhi and extended his hand in friendship.

"No more call me king, my lord," Limhi said humbly and bowed before Mosiah. "I—and my people—would be thy humble subjects, if you will have us. I was chosen to be king among my people during a time of bondage and hardship, but through the grace of God we have been delivered. We now place ourselves at your mercy."

"Very well. I will most happily be your king and serve your people." Mosiah smiled at Limhi, offering a hand to raise him up. "Come now, we have much to discuss. I want to learn all that has happened among your people."

Limhi brought forth the records of his people and presented them to the king. Mosiah reverently handled all the records, but his eyes rested on the twenty-four golden plates. He nodded toward them and said, "I am most particularly interested in the writing on these plates. Ammon tells me you found them in the north country." He smiled slightly. "I am in possession of a stone that my grandfather obtained. The writing on it is very similar to these mysterious plates."

Mosiah seemed lost in thought for a moment as he surveyed the golden pages. "This is a great blessing from the Lord," he said, looking up at Limhi. "As are you and your people. We will spend the coming weeks finding new homes for all of you and establishing you in the land. But for now, let us eat and talk and praise God for His goodness to our peoples."

Only a few months passed before another miraculous event occurred—an emissary arrived to announce the coming of Alma and his people from their home in the Lamanite highlands. This was a blessing prayed for by all the people of God, for it would finally reunite all who belonged to the Church of God. The valley was filled with excitement, and a large crowd turned out to greet Alma and his people. Along with King Mosiah, the first among them was Limhi.

"Do you remember me?" Limhi asked hesitantly as he approached Alma. Beside him, people were surging forward to welcome those that they had once known in the land of Nephi.

Alma smiled broadly, extending his hand. "I most certainly do, Limhi, son of Noah. I'd heard you were now leading the people and that you'd escaped to this land."

Limhi took Alma's hand, looking astonished. "How have you heard this?"

"We recently spent some time with Amulon, your father's chief priest, but that is a long story meant for another time," Alma replied.

"Alma," Limhi said softly. "Much has happened since those days in the land of Nephi. We—my people and I—were hardhearted. I am so sorry for not listening to the words of the Lord." Limhi fell to his knees and began to sob. "Will you forgive me?"

Alma immediately knelt beside Limhi and embraced him. "Of course," he said quietly.

Wiping the tears from his eyes, Limhi raised himself up. "Then," he said looking Alma in the eye, "I and my people wish to enter into the waters of baptism and to make a covenant to serve God and keep His commandments. We have waited a long time for this privilege. Will you grant us our petition?"

Alma smiled broadly and again wrapped his arms around Limhi. This time, however, the tears were his.

The Nephites were once again united in one nation. King Mosiah gathered his people together and read the records of Zeniff and Alma. When all had been spoken, Limhi and his people finally entered the waters of baptism, adding their names to the Church of God.

Endnotes

1 The only way for the men of Ammon to be mistaken for priests of Noah is if Limhi did not get a good look at them. Mosiah 7:10 tells us that they were surrounded by the king's guard and committed to prison, so perhaps Limhi only saw that men who had been traveling in the wilderness were approaching, and then the guards took them away. Otherwise Limhi would have certainly recognized that they were not priests of his father.

2 It is difficult to know why Ammon would consider himself an "unworthy servant" (Mosiah 21:33) when responding to Limhi's desire to be baptized. To his credit, Limhi understands the importance of having the proper authority. Ammon does not dispute the fact that he has the authority. He simply states that he is unworthy.

What does Ammon mean by that phrase? He preaches the words of King Benjamin (Mosiah 8:3) and desires to join himself with Alma in the Church of God (Mosiah 21:33). He seems like a righteous fellow, so why does he say he is unworthy? I don't know the answer to that question, but I wonder if he considered himself unworthy to baptize someone as important as a king. Perhaps he didn't think he was at the right social standing to do so. Perhaps he felt he needed permission from his governing priesthood authority (although that still wouldn't explain the "unworthy servant" comment). It might also be a straightforward example of how blessings are forfeited when priesthood holders do not keep themselves worthy to use their priesthood.

In a dire war with a bloodthirsty madman, four captains would rise to the occasion in support of their prophet and their nation.

11

Zeram, Amnor, Manti, and Limher
Alma's Loyal Captains

❦ Alma 2–3 ❦

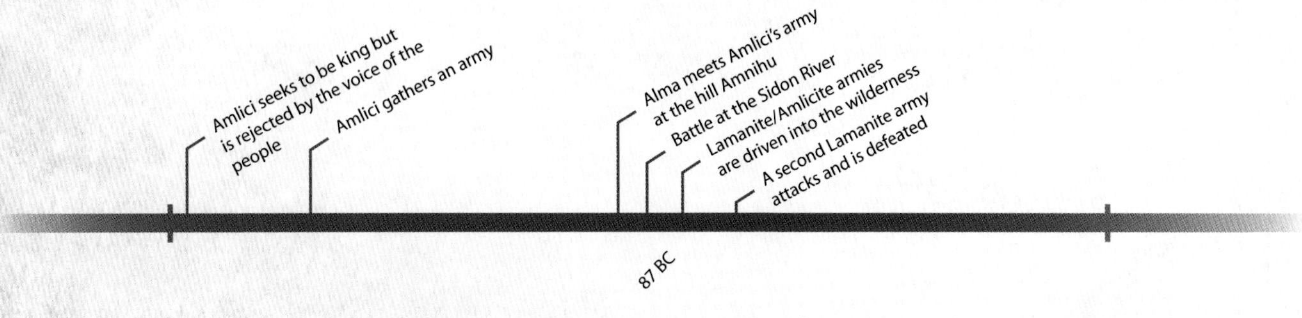

Amlici seeks to be king but is rejected by the voice of the people

Amlici gathers an army

Alma meets Amlici's army at the hill Amnihu

Battle at the Sidon River

Lamanite/Amlicite armies are driven into the wilderness

A second Lamanite army attacks and is defeated

87 BC

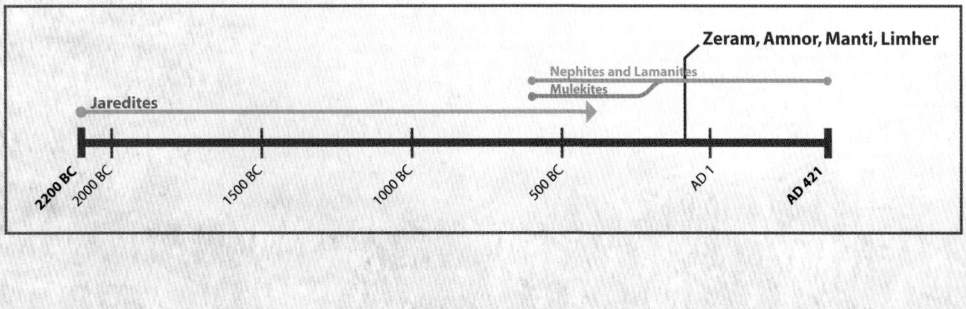

Jaredites

Nephites and Lamanites
Mulekites

Zeram, Amnor, Manti, Limher

2200 BC 2000 BC 1500 BC 1000 BC 500 BC AD 1 AD 421

An old woman drained the water from her bowl and poured the seeds on a mealing stone. Then she gripped another stone, this one smooth and rounded, and ground the seeds into a bright red paste.[1] When she had finished, Amlici ran his fingers through the mixture, nodding his approval.

Straightening to his full stature, he looked over the vast assembly of his people. Tens of thousands[2] had gathered, and all were willing to give their lives so that he could be made their king and rule over all the land of the Nephites. Amlici smiled in satisfaction. He knew that, dressed in his grandest apparel, he already looked the part. It was only a matter of time before it was made official.

He drew his fingers across his forehead, marking himself with the red paste. Then he raised his fist high in the air and declared, "We are not Nephites. We are not Lamanites. We are a people unto ourselves! With this mark upon our foreheads, we are *Amlicites!*"

Just as Amlici had hoped, his speech drew enthusiastic cheers from the crowd. Since the

beginning, these people had been drawn to him by the power of his words. He had preached often within the city, exhorting the people to rise up from the bonds of fear and trembling before the God of the Nephites. He had called for them to lift up their heads and rejoice, for all would be saved and have eternal life. In turn, the people had given him riches and wealth.[3]

Now, as one body, the crowd surged forward, eager to mark themselves in a covenant of their loyalty.[4]

Amlici continued. "You have made me your king. I would have already been made king over all the land if the *people of God*, as they suppose themselves to be, had not come out against me.[5] But, that makes no difference now. We shall destroy these people and free our brothers from the bondage of their religion. Then we shall all be one people and the mightiest nation under heaven!" Again the people cheered, louder than before. Amlici waited a moment and then silenced them with a wave of his hands.

"Gather your weapons of war and prepare for what is to come. On the morrow, we will meet upon the Hill Amnihu, for there our enemies will come to us. It is there that we will bring down the hammer of judgment upon all those who oppose us!" The crowd's shout of approval could no longer be quieted, and it broke forth like the crashing of a massive wave on the shore.

In the land of Zarahemla, the people of Alma were also preparing for war. Alma, accompanied by his attendants, walked through a large courtyard that had been converted into a massive armory. It was now filled with weapons of war of every kind—swords and cimeters, bows and arrows, and slings alongside mounds of smooth round stones. As Alma neared the edge of the courtyard, he joined a group of men—captains—who were both proven and skilled. They had been charged with defending the liberty of his people. As soon as they saw Alma, each captain paid the chief judge his respects with a small bow. Then they gathered around to receive his instruction.

Alma looked at each of the righteous men carefully before making his announcement, "I will lead the army into battle."

After their initial shocked silence, the captains erupted in tender protest. Alma listened for a moment to their concerns for his safety and then said, "I am the chief judge and the governor of the people of Nephi—"

"But you are also the high priest over our church," interrupted one captain.

"Yes, Captain Manti," Alma replied calmly.

"You have been raised as your father before you," tried another captain. "He was a great high priest and leader of men but . . ." He trailed off, his face reddening slightly.

"He was not a warrior? Is that what you wish to say, Captain Zeram?" Alma offered. Zeram lowered his head meekly, indicating that he meant no offense.[6]

"Zeram and Manti, Amnor and Limher, and all my valiant captains,"[7] Alma addressed them. "You have been chosen to lead our forces into battle to protect our nation not only because of your skills as warriors, but also because each of you is endowed with the Spirit of God."[8] Alma looked at each man in turn. "This is not merely a battle against flesh and blood. It is a battle against the rulers of darkness in this world. The Spirit of God is our sword, and faith is our shield.[9] When I lead you forth to battle—and *I will* lead you—and when you, in turn, lead your men, you must be armed with the power of God. That is where our true strength lies, and that is how we will preserve the liberty of our people from men like Amlici."

The captains faced Alma, steeled to their purpose. Their eyes were bright with a renewed understanding of the task that lay before them. They would not fail. With God at their side, they *could not* fail!

The following morning Alma, thronged by his captains and a great army of men, crossed the River Sidon near the city of Zarahemla, where the water was calm and shallow.[10] They continued onward until they reached the Hill Amnihu—where they saw Amlici and his army standing ready to receive them upon the hill itself.

When Alma saw concern on the faces of some of his men, he turned to them and said in a loud voice. "They may have the advantage of higher ground, but we shall be strengthened by what we fight for and who we fight with! The power that supports us gives us an advantage they cannot foresee! So let us now appeal to our great God and defend our religion and our freedom!"

The battle began. Two armies—one fighting for power and the other fighting to throw it down—clashed their weapons of war on the Hill Amnihu. Amlici's advantage and the strength of his warriors were great, and the Nephites began to fall before them. But the Lord strengthened the hand of the Nephites, and soon the tides began to turn. For every Nephite who fell, two of Amlici's men were cut down.[11] Before

long their enemies could no longer stand their ground, and they began to flee before the might of the men of Alma. The Nephites pursued them all that day, slaying a vast number of them. Eventually it became too dark to give chase any longer, and they stopped to set up camp in the Valley of Gideon.

That night when Alma called his captains together to commend them for their valiant efforts in the battle and to determine their next move, the chief captain, Zoram[12] stepped forward. Holding his helmet in his hands, he spoke with fervor. "We cannot let Amlici escape into the wilderness. He has proven the depth of his treachery and his power to set men against us with only his words." He turned to Alma, staring at him with urgency in his gaze. "We must send men into the wilderness to follow him and bring us word of his location."

Before anyone could even utter another word, four men stood forward to accept the dangerous task.

"Zeram, Amnor, Manti, and Limher," Alma named them one by one. "You have fought all day and pursued our enemy with vigor. Surely you are hungry and weary, and yet . . . you would take this important mission upon yourselves?"

"This and more to defend our people," Manti responded earnestly. The others nodded their assent.

"Go, then. We will await your return," Alma said in a voice of solemn gratitude, then he briefly

laid a hand on each man's shoulder. "May God be with you," Alma whispered to them in prayer. Then each captain, with his men, disappeared into the night.

As the first rays of sunlight broke through the trees, Alma and his men began to break camp. The mood among them was hopeful—having severely crippled Amlici's forces, they had little doubt that the battle this day would be brief. But as the captains began gathering their men together, shouts were heard from within the forest.

Zeram and his fellow captains broke into the valley, running as if the army of Amlici was on their heels. The men of the camp watched first in alarm—grasping their swords and looking around wildly for their leaders—and then in confusion. The four captains were alone. No one was chasing them, yet they dodged men and tents and did not stop in their flight until they found Alma.

Amnor was the first to speak, trying to communicate as clearly as he could, while the others gasped and tried to catch their breath.

"We followed . . . the Amlicites . . . and then . . . in the land of Minon . . . we saw a numerous host . . . of Lamanites . . ."

A curious crowd had already begun to gather around the men, but at the mention of the Lamanites, everyone within earshot hurried over to listen in on the report. Amnor was wheezing now and unable to continue.

Manti quickly looked up. His entire body seemed to be shaking. "The Amlicites have joined them!"

A ripple of panic spread through the ranks, and Alma nodded toward his chief captain, Zoram, who immediately began organizing the men.

Alma turned back to Manti, his expression filled with determination and dread. "What is the direction of their march?"

"They have attacked the land of Minon, and the people are fleeing before them with their flocks and their wives and their children." Manti reached out and grasped Alma's arm. "They are marching toward Zarahemla—except we make haste our enemies will obtain possession of our city. Our fathers and our wives and our children will all be slain!" Manti, no longer able to stand, fell to the earth.

Several men hurried forward to attend to the exhausted scouts. "Rest yourselves now," Alma said to his four captains. Then, raising his voice to address his whole host, he added, "We will not let Zarahemla fall!"

Within the hour, the troops had begun marching toward Zarahemla. The only obstacle barring their path was the mighty River Sidon.[13] Crossing was far from ideal, but the troops could not spare the time needed to march farther downstream. They had to intercept the invading army. As long as their enemies did not pin them down while they were crossing the water, they stood a chance.

As they forded the river, Alma and his captains kept a sharp eye out for any sign of their illusive enemy. A movement on the shoreline caught Alma's attention just before they reached the western bank. Alma silently raised a hand for his captains to halt, his gaze riveted straight ahead. His men held their breath, waiting silently. Then Alma's face darkened as Amlici stepped arrogantly into view on the shore, laughing at the chief judge and his men as they waded through the river.

"Did you think you'd won?" Amlici shouted, his features twisted in a gruesome smile. "Did you think your God had given you power?" he jeered, staring directly at Alma as a tide of warriors began to appear all around him, weapons at the ready.

Amlici cocked his head to the side. "You thought we were in your power, didn't you?" His laugh was echoed by the men on all sides of him. Amlici delighted in the sound. "But all the while we were leading you farther and farther from Zarahemla, the seat of all your of power." Then, for a moment, he grew dangerously quiet and advanced toward Alma. "It is true that I lost many more soldiers than I had planned yesterday," he acknowledged. "But I draw comfort from an alliance I made with those of . . . similar interests."[14]

The king of the Lamanites stepped forward, sneering at the army stranded in the river.

"Now let's see your God deliver you out of our hands!" Amlici mocked.

As Alma stood waist-deep in the river, wave after wave of Lamanites became visible. It was impossible to number them.

Alma pointed his sword at Amlici. "Mock our God at your own peril," he shouted. Then, turning to his own men, he said most earnestly, "Trust in God." He faced Amlici again, raised his sword to the sky, and charged.

The armies met on the west bank, where the enemy's vast army immediately succeeded in pushing Alma and his captains farther back into the river. Eager for a chance to challenge Alma and slay the priest with his own hands, Amlici led his troops.

Alma and his men fought bravely but desperately as they struggled to keep their balance in the water. Alma glanced to his side and saw Amlici, weapon raised, only a few feet away. He pivoted, raising his own sword just in time to deflect the blow.

Alma drew in a sharp breath. He quickly found himself outmatched by both the ferocity of Amlici's attacks and his skill of combat. With every stroke he felt himself becoming sluggish and predictable in his defense. As he stumbled on a river rock and tumbled backward into the water, he was certain his end was near. But as Amlici rushed forward to slay the high priest, four captains rushed ahead to protect their fallen leader.

"What have we here, my brothers?" called out Limher. "It seems we are the presence of something most foul—a king with a vile stench!"

Amlici was enraged—a predator separated from its prey.

"Foul indeed," continued Manti. "Allow us to bathe you!" They charged forward to attack.

A rush of gratitude filled Alma's heart, and he took the brief respite to call upon his God. "O Lord, have mercy and spare my life, that I may be an instrument in thy hands to save and preserve this people."

As Alma struggled to his feet, he saw that Amlici had all but broken through the barrier his loyal captains had made. Manti had fallen, his hand raised to a wound on his face. Limher had been struck by an arrow, and Zeram and Amnor were giving way. Filled with renewed determination, Alma rushed forward in the strength of the Lord. Amlici fell back before him in surprise, losing his advantage as Alma blocked his weapon with powerful blows. The chief judge fought with such strength that, for the first time, Amlici's face showed fear. The realization that Alma was truly being supported by God came too late to save Amlici, and as Alma dealt his final blow, the would-be king fell upon the muddy west bank of the Sidon.

When the Lamanite king, who had been pushing ahead to offer Alma a challenge of his own, saw Amlici fall to the ground, a look of anger and fear clouded his face. As he came within striking range, Alma's first blow caught on his shield, sending the king stumbling to the side.

The king was already favoring his sword arm, the result of a fresh injury.[15] With one last glance in Alma's direction, he let out a desperate cry and retreated. Nearby guards quickly replaced

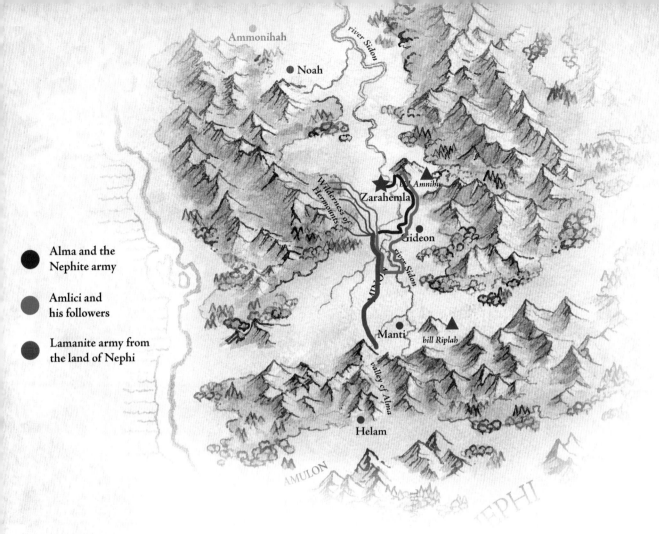

Alma and the
Nephite army

Amlici and
his followers

Lamanite army from
the land of Nephi

their master as he fled before Alma's blade, but the high priest was far from outnumbered. Zeram and Amnor hurried to their leader's aid with other captains following close behind.[16] Within mere minutes, the last guard had fallen victim to a Nephite's sword.

Pushing forward, Alma's forces began to take the west bank, and it was not long before the enemy forces gave way. As Lamanites and Amlicites fled in fear before the Nephite army, Alma offered a silent prayer of gratitude. There was no doubt in his mind that the power of God had been at work this day. An enemy that could not be numbered had set a fiendish trap for the Nephites, and the outcome had been nothing short of a miracle.

No matter which way the enemy tried to retreat, they were met on every hand, smitten and driven by the might of the Nephites. Those scattered forces that remained fled to the northwest and into a wilderness where the Nephites would not follow. At the forest's borders, Alma ordered his men to regroup and attend to the injured. The battle was over. Amlici's treachery had been unraveled. The land was safe.

"We can't just let them go," a young warrior named Jarem said. Manti, who was nursing the wound on his face, looked up wearily and tried to sound patient in his response.

"This is the wilderness of Hermounts," he said, indicating the tree line. "Haven't you heard about what lies within its borders?" Jarem shook his head, so Manti continued. "This dark wilderness is infested by wild and ravenous beasts. It is said that those who walk beneath its murky canopy do not return to the land of the living. All that remains to tell their sorry tale . . . is their bones."[17] The young warrior looked toward the wilderness, his eyes wide. Then he slowly nodded, acknowledging the wisdom of Alma's decision.

Zoram sat down beside Manti with a groan. "Could you be any more dramatic?" he asked, shaking his head. Jarem frowned, thinking now that he had fallen for a jest.

"Is it not true, then?" he asked, and Manti smiled just a little.

"This is the wilderness of Hermounts," Zoram explained, "and we are wise to let the Lamanites and the Amlicites flee. Many of them will never again see the light of day, and those who escape will not return to our land." He examined Manti's wound, and, satisfied that it did not need immediate attention, stood up. "Come, Manti. Our chief judge, the governor of our land and high priest of our church, wishes to commend you and your fellow captains and for your remarkable service."

"But, Captain . . ." Jarem called after them, still glancing back at the haunting wilderness. Manti and Zoram had already disappeared into the crowd of men who were cheering for the mighty captains.

Some time later, after peace had been restored to the land, Jarem learned that Manti's words contained more truth than he'd realized. When he was assigned to a team charged with the task of entering the wilderness of Hermounts, he discovered the bones of men who had been devoured by the beasts and vultures of the wilderness. The soldiers gathered the bones and piled them into heaps, which remained as a monument to those who had attempted to destroy the freedom of the people of Nephi—and as a warning to those who sought to destroy the servants of God.

While many Lamanites were seeking for war among the Nephites, one group in the land of Ishmael was taking part in a dramatic change of heart, due, in part, to the remarkable faith of a king and his beloved queen—but that's another story.

Endnotes

1 The mealing stone is known as a "metate" in Mesoamerica, and the handheld stone is called a "mano." The seeds described are from an Achiote (Bixa orellana) tree. These seeds were used anciently to make a natural pigment (annatto) that, among other things, was used as a red body paint. (Jose Rafael Lovera, *Food Culture in South America.* Westport CT: Greenwood Press, 2005, 51). Another source of red pigment used in paints in the Americas was iron oxide, found in some clays.

2 I propose this number based on the only number reference we have for the size of Amlici's army. Alma 2:19 tells us that 12,532 of Amlici's men were killed after the first day of battle. Alma 2:2 describes that "many" people (men and women) were led away by Amlici. I think it is fair to suppose an army of men of at least 20,000 (more than half killed would certainly be a "slaughter" as described in verse 19). So the group Amlici is addressing at the opening of my story would consist of not just battle-worthy men, but older men and women and children. Hence the proposal of "tens of thousands."

3 Amlici was after the order of Nehor (Alma 2:1), and these teachings were his (Alma 1:3–6).

4 Alma 3:4.

5 When Amlici gained enough support, he challenged the newly formed system of judges and endeavored to be king. The people of Nephi voted on the matter, and the voice of the people came out against the political reformation, although there was great contention on both sides of the issue (Alma 2:2–7). It wasn't just the people of the Church of God who were against Amlici, however, but all those who had not been drawn away after Amlici's fair promises (Alma 2:3).

6 It is uncertain what training in warfare Alma had. Obviously he did well enough as shown by this story, but this appears to be the first and last time he leads the Nephite military forces or goes to war in any form.

7 Alma 2:13 says that the Nephites appointed captains, higher captains, and chief captains according to their numbers. Zeram, Amnor, Manti, and Limher seem to be captains of some kind, as Alma 2:22 mentions that they have command over "their men." I am fascinated that Mormon, who is telling us this story in Alma 2, thinks so highly of these men that he wants to be sure we know their names.

8   3 Nephi 3:19.

9   Ephesians 6:12, 16–17.

10 We know the Sidon flows northward through most or all of its length because it is consistently described as having banks on the east and the west. The head of the river (where a river starts as described in 1 Nephi 8:17) is in the south wilderness (Alma 22:27; 43:22) and flows down toward the sea.

There are certain places in the Book of Mormon where the people cross the River Sidon. I propose that not all areas were equally accessible based on my own experiences canoeing and exploring rivers in the Midwest. It's fairly flat where I live, and yet a river changes and takes on a life of its own as it moves through the landscape. In Book of Mormon lands there were much more dramatic landscapes, and so I suspect that the Sidon was even more diverse—sometimes shallow, sometimes rapid, sometimes deep and slow. That said, the common crossing point mentioned seems to be the one by the city of Zarahemla (Alma 2:15; 6:7; 8:3) but the record also mentions one south of Manti, by the headwaters in the mountainous south wilderness (Alma 16:6–7; 43:27–41). Because the Book of Mormon only mentions these crossing places specifically I propose that they were the most commonly used and that there were many other places that were difficult or impossible to cross.

11 It wasn't exactly a two-to-one ratio. When the battle was done 12,532 of the Amlicites were killed and 6,562 (Alma 2:19) of the Nephites perished, so it's actually a 1:1.9 ratio, but you get the idea.

12 Zoram isn't mentioned in the text until six years later (Alma 16:5), but in my mind there is no reason he couldn't be the chief captain six years before he is first mentioned by name. I think he'd appreciate it.

13 One of the reasons why I think there must not have been a lot of other options for crossing the Sidon is that Amlici seemed to know right where Alma and his men would be. What are the chances he would happen to show up at exactly that spot?

14 This is another situation where there are just too many coincidences for it not to mean something. What are the chances that Amlici would be fleeing from a battle and just happen upon a massive Lamanite invasion force headed toward Zarahemla and that those Lamanites would let Amlici and his men unite with them—no questions asked? It's highly suspect in my view. I think some shady dealings were going on. Perhaps the fact that the Amlicites were marking their foreheads with red (just like the Lamanites did (Alma 3:4) was a sign that they were already in league with one another.

15 I am assuming that this king, with his innumerable army, was the king over all the Lamanites and not just one of the subordinate Lamanite kings—like Lamoni (Alma 17:21), Antiomno (Alma 20:4), or Amulon (Mosiah 23:39). If this is the case, this king would be Lamoni's father, who had recently survived an encounter with Ammon, which disabled the use of his arm (Alma 20:20). This is all assuming that the timetables, as we understand them, are correct. It appears that the old king had time and motivation to launch two attacks against the Nephites (Alma 2:27–38; 3:20–23) between the time of his encounter with Ammon and his being taught the gospel by Aaron in Alma 22, which led to his conversion.

These attacks may be one reason why Anti-Nephi-Lehi, who becomes king after his father dies and who quite possibly helped initiate and fight in these wars against the Nephites, is so reluctant (perhaps being guilt-ridden) to ask them for mercy when Ammon suggests that they move the Lamanite converts to the lands of the Nephites (Alma 27:8). If you are not familiar with this story, read Alma 17–27, in particular Alma 27:4–14.

16 Alma 2:32–33.

17 Alma 2:37–38 describes this wilderness in a more dramatic way than any other landmark in the Book of Mormon. It is "infested by wild and ravenous beasts" that join with vultures in devouring corpses, and on its borders are piles made of the bones of men—it sounds creepy. This was not a landmark to go unnoticed.

*N*ever had Ammon seen a faith like hers among all the Nephites—faith seemed like all she had left.

12 *L*amoni's *W*ife
Faith Beyond the Nephites'

❖ *A*lma 19 ❖

Ammon and his brothers arrive in the land of Nephi

Lamoni, his wife, and many of his people are converted

Two armies of wicked Lamanites attack the Nephites

Wicked Lamanites attack the people of Ammon—many Lamanites join the people of Ammon

Wicked Lamanites war with the Nephites, are defeated, and return to join the people of Ammon

Lamanite converts are welcomed among the Nephites

90 BC   85 BC   80 BC   75 BC

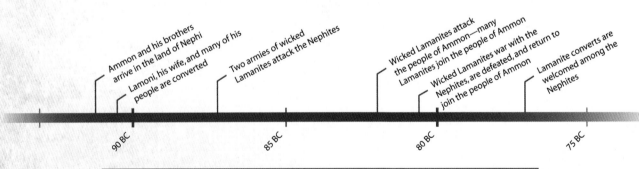

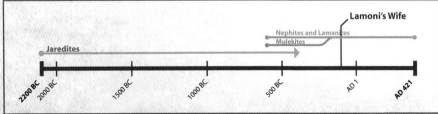

Lamoni's Wife

Nephites and Lamanites
Mulekites

Jaredites

2200 BC 2000 BC   1500 BC   1000 BC   500 BC   AD 1   AD 421

"The sepulchre is ready, my queen," the priest said in a somber tone. "It is time."

Namiah looked up from the bed of her husband only briefly. King Lamoni, her husband, did not stir. She draped her arms across his chest tenderly, protectively.

"A little more time," she whispered.

The priest took a step closer. "It has been two days and two nights, my queen. The king must be placed in the sepulchre. His soul is gone, and . . ." He hesitated. "And the smell of death is upon him."

Namiah slowly raised her head and glared up at the priest. *No*," she said in a voice filled with warning. The word echoed through the chamber, and the priest lowered his eyes, unwilling to meet her gaze. After a brief moment, he and his fellow servants turned away and quietly retreated.

The queen laid her head on Lamoni's chest and slowly inhaled. He was not gone. The smell of death was not there. Not to her.[1]

Gathering her strength, she wiped the tears that seemed to be ever present on her cheeks. "Abish," she said in a low voice without looking up, knowing her servant girl would be near. "Send for the Nephite."

The Nephite, Ammon, had recently made his home among the Lamanites. Namiah thought of him with a sense of both puzzlement and curiosity. It was said he was a prince among his people[2]—so why he had come to dwell with the Lamanites in the land of Ishmael as a servant to her husband had been a matter of great debate among the royal house.

She recalled the day Ammon had turned down Lamoni's invitation to form an alliance by marrying one of their daughters. Instead, Ammon had volunteered to serve the king. More than a few eyebrows had been raised, but Ammon seemed content to labor in the service of his new people.[3]

Three days later, the servants had returned from the hills wide-eyed, with an unbelievable story. They told of how Ammon had defended the flocks of the king against robbers in a most remarkable way, having shown forth great power and strength. Truly he could not be slain by the enemies of the king. They called Ammon the prophet of a holy God and told all who would listen how he had power to do many mighty works in this God's name. King Lamoni had listened to every word.[4]

When the servants had finished, Lamoni had sent for Ammon, desiring to learn more of this God of the Nephites. The servants related to the queen that after listening for some time as Ammon told him of the great God of heaven, Lamoni had fallen to his knees in prayer. Then the king had inexplicably fallen to the ground as if he were dead.[5]

Namiah swallowed hard. She hadn't been there when Lamoni had collapsed, and none of the servants could adequately explain what had happened.[6] For the last two days and two nights she had sat by his bedside in tears and confusion, not knowing what was wrong or how to help her husband.

She met Ammon in the throne room of the palace, but she swept her hand through the air dismissively when he bowed before her. She had no desire to put on airs. She could not summon the pride and arrogance her position afforded her. Today, and for the past two days, she was less a queen and more a wife, stricken with grief and desperate for hope.

"What would the great queen of the Lamanites desire of me?" Ammon spoke with no pretension. The confidence of his demeanor was not laced with arrogance but with humility.

Namiah was surprised by the sincerity in his voice. She felt he truly wished to serve her. Her collected countenance almost dissolved as she filled with gratitude at his words, but she steadied herself and leveled her gaze upon Ammon.

"I would that ye should go in and see my husband."

Ammon bowed humbly and followed the queen from the throne room. As they entered the king's bedchamber, Ammon's eyes rested on Lamoni's still features. Joy—not sorrow—filled his heart.

Ammon's mind went back in the not-so-distant past when another man he knew lay as if dead. Alma, his friend, had strayed from the path of righteousness and was lost in sin—but not lost to God. A dark veil of unbelief had to be cast from his mind to allow the glorious light of everlasting joy to illuminate his soul. The experience had been so overwhelming that Alma's physical body had collapsed to the ground. He had lain as though dead for three days before he recovered.[7]

A slight smile touched Ammon's lips, and he turned to the queen. "He is not dead, but he sleepeth in God, and on the morrow he shall rise again; therefore bury him not." He spoke with confidence, but the queen's expression was unreadable. "Believest thou this?" he asked.

Namiah was still, seeming to search her own feelings before she answered. "I have had no witness save thy word, and the word of our servants; nevertheless I believe that it shall be according as thou hast said."

Ammon nodded, Namiah's simple testimony filling his soul with joy. "Blessed art thou because of thy exceeding faith; I say unto thee, woman, there has not been such great faith among all the people of the Nephites." Ammon did not offer this compliment lightly. The queen believed God's promise to her with no proof other than the word of a servant. And she would be blessed—she and her entire nation.

Namiah did not leave her husband's side all that night. She watched over him, Ammon's words ever-present in her mind. *He is not dead, but he sleepeth in God . . . on the morrow he shall rise again . . . Blessed art thou because of thy exceeding faith . . .*

The next day dawned, and as the time arrived that Ammon had appointed, Namiah looked steadfastly upon Lamoni's face. All was still, and then . . . her heart leaped as Lamoni's head moved slightly. His eyes opened, as if he were awakening from a most wonderful dream. As Lamoni blinked in the light of day, his gaze locked on his greatest treasure—his wife. Her beautiful face looked down on him.

A collective gasp filled the room, and the queen briefly looked back at the servants who had gathered. Turning again to her husband, Namiah took his hand. She had never seen such a look in her husband's eyes when he gazed at her. There had never been such love there before. It was as if he could see into her soul and he'd found such worth and beauty there. The king raised himself up and gently brought his hand to her face. Lifting his eyes to heaven, he said, "Blessed be the name of God!" Then he looked intently into Namiah's eyes and added, "And blessed art thou."

The queen's brow furrowed slightly. Surely God should be praised, but why in the same breath would Lamoni praise her? What had he experienced?

"For as sure as thou livest," Lamoni continued sincerely, piercing her with the intensity of his gaze, "I have seen my Redeemer." The king's voice shook with emotion, but he continued. "And he shall come forth, and be born of a woman." He stroked the queen's cheek tenderly. "And he shall redeem all mankind who believe on his name."

His words pierced her very soul. A marvelous spirit filled the room. She could neither explain nor deny it. Lamoni's declaration about a Savior and about the divinity of women in God's plan ran through her mind again, and the queen was overcome by the holy Spirit of God. The Redeemer of all mankind would enter the world through a woman. Namiah sank down beside her husband, joy filling her soul.

The Spirit was poured out upon all those in attendance as well, including Ammon, and they too fell to the earth. As stillness descended on the room once again, only one figure stood among the fallen—Abish, the servant of the queen.[8]

Abish, a believer herself, ran to gather others, hope filling her heart that they would see what had happened and believe in the one true God. She did not expect that once the people had arrived, there would be controversy over what it all meant—the king, queen, and servants were all lying as if they were dead, and a Nephite rested in the midst of them.[9] The people began to argue among themselves, and Abish's heart was filled with anguish as the contention grew more heated. Finally, with tears in her eyes, she stepped forward. Hoping to awaken the queen, she reached out and took her by the hand.

Namiah awoke immediately and rose to her feet, stopping the contention by declaring with a loud voice, "O blessed Jesus, who has saved me from an awful hell! O blessed God, have mercy on this people!"

Everyone stared in silence as the queen, her expression radiating joy, clasped her hands and began to speak words that sounded angelic but could not be understood by the people.[10] It was as if she were communicating directly with heaven. Namiah then turned and took her husband by the hand. He too arose and began ministering to his people, teaching them the great things he had learned. Ammon and the servants also arose and joined the king in declaring that their hearts had been changed. Many believed their testimonies, and soon after a great number of them were baptized. Shortly after that, they established a church in the land.

This was just the beginning of the great work the Lord was about to bring forth among the Lamanites. In the coming years, He would continue to pour out His Spirit among them. This work altered the very history of the Lamanites and Nephites and led to the salvation of countless souls. And it all started with the willingness of a righteous young man to serve, the desire of a king to know, and the gift of a queen to believe.

Lamoni's and his wife's examples and passion for the Church of God helped convert thousands, including Lamoni's father, who was king over all the Lamanites. This people became a strong community of believers who were so immovable in their faith that when enemies gathered to destroy them, they buried their weapons of war rather than fight. About one thousand faithful Lamanites died in the conflict that followed. We do not know whether or not Lamoni and his wife survived this attack (there is no mention of either of them in the scriptures that follow), but if they did give their lives that day, surely their example inspired others to abandon wickedness and repent of their sins. Of the attacking forces, more than a thousand threw down their weapons and joined the people of God.[11]

Not long after the battle, these righteous Lamanites were adopted into the Nephite nation. They were called "the people of Ammon" from that time onward, and they were a blessing to all those who had contact with them. In fact, it was the loving arms of this community that brought forth the heroic two thousand sixty stripling warriors—but that's another story.

Endnotes

1   In our modern age, the understanding of the importance of smell has virtually been lost. Many studies have been conducted in recent years that show that scents have an amazing capacity for influencing our behavior—especially that of women. It is a well published phenomenon that women have an increased sense of smell during pregnancy, but even more applicable to the story of Lamoni's wife is a recent study that strongly suggests women (not men) use smell as an important factor in choosing a mate (*Psychological Science* 17:830). When Lamoni's wife says she doesn't think her husband is dead because of his smell, she knows what she is talking about.

2   Ammon was the son of the late King Mosiah. By the time he and his brothers left on their missions, their father, the king, was nearing the end of his life. He died shortly after his sons left to go to the land of the Lamanites (Mosiah 28:8–9; 29:2–3). While the sons of Mosiah were on their missions, the monarchy was dissolved and a system of judges was put in place. Whether the Lamanites were familiar with this major political change or not, Ammon's familial connections to the former ruling family would have made him an important guest and a unique servant.

3   Alma 17:19–25.

4   Alma 17:26–18:4. If you are not familiar with the story of how Ammon protected the flocks of the king, it is a must-read.

5   Alma 18:14–42.

6   After Lamoni fell to the earth, the servants actually had to take his body to the queen (whose name is fictional in this book) and lay him on his bed. The queen and her children "greatly lamented his loss" (Alma 18:43). It's unclear why no one blamed Ammon for the king's fall or why no one seemed to talk to him for the next two days. Perhaps they were too intimidated or afraid because of the godlike power Ammon had shown in defending the king's flocks and in the power of his preaching. Ammon's brother Aaron didn't benefit from that same courtesy when he taught Lamoni's father sometime after these events. However, Lamoni's father had a similar response to hearing the gospel message. He also fell to the earth. His wife, the queen, tried to have Aaron killed (Alma 22:19). It seems like this would be a natural response. Lamoni's people, on the other hand, treated Ammon very gently.

7   Mosiah 27:11–24; Alma 36:6–23.

8   Abish has a story all her own. Many readers will already be familiar with it, but if you are not, read what little is known about her past in Alma 19:16–17.

9   A significant event happens during this time. A brother of one of the robbers (the leader) who was killed by Ammon tries to exact revenge by attacking Ammon while he lay on the ground. The Lord, however, strikes the brother down before he can do so. The watchful crowd is really not sure how to respond (Alma 19:21–22).

10   It appears that the Holy Ghost had granted the queen the gift of tongues. If this is the case, it is a singular event in the Book of Mormon. Certainly the Nephites understood this gift (see 2 Nephi 31:13; Alma 9:21; 3 Nephi 29:6; Moroni 10:15), but there is not a specific description of anyone being given this gift the way it is related in Alma 19:30. The closest similarity I am familiar with would be when God the Father speaks from heaven in 3 Nephi 11:3–7. He spoke twice and still the people did not understand his words. Perhaps this was the same reason why the Lamanites did not understand the queen's heavenly speech—they hadn't yet opened their ears.

11   The Lamanites who did not join the people of Ammon after the attack went on to attack the Nephites and were defeated. Many of those Lamanites returned to the land of Ishmael, buried their weapons of war, and then joined the people of God. The example set by the people of Ammon was even more far-reaching than just in converting those warriors who joined right after the initial attack (Alma 25:1–14).

A leader of the resistance against the Lamanite king's desire for war, he was prepared to make a stand, but what he got was not a fair fight.

13 Lehonti
Betrayed by Treachery

❖ Alma 47 ❖

Zerahemnah leads Lamanites against Captain Moroni's men

Defeated Lamanite warriors make a covenant of peace

Helaman and his brethren preach in every city

Amalickiah seeks to become king of the Nephites

Amalickiah is rejected and flees to the Lamanites

Lehonti refuses to fight against the Nephites

Amalickiah becomes king of the Lamanites

Lamanites attack Ammonihah

73 BC
19th YotJ

72 BC
20th YotJ

Lehonti

Nephites and Lamanites

Mulekites

Jaredites

2200 BC
2000 BC
1500 BC
1000 BC
500 BC
AD 1
AD 421

Soldiers from both sides stared as a Nephite lifted the Lamanite scalp off the ground by its now-matted black hair and laid it across the tip of his sword. His eyes scanned the crowd as he raised it up for all to see. Then he cried, "Even as this scalp has fallen to the earth, which is the scalp of your chief, so shall ye fall to the earth except ye will deliver up your weapons of war and depart with a covenant of peace."

Lehonti, a Lamanite warrior,[1] grimaced at the sight of his leader's scalp being held aloft. Then he saw the bodies. During the battle he had thought only of survival. Any hopes he may have had for overcoming the Nephites and forcing them into bondage evaporated when he caught sight of their breastplates and shields. The Lamanites had weapons, but little else to protect their bare bodies. Lehonti had been able to ignore the growing number of his fallen brethren, but now—now that their attempted retreat had failed miserably and Nephites surrounded them on all sides—now he saw the bodies. Once the work of death had commenced, the Nephite swords had delivered it at almost every stroke. Lehonti glanced over the sea of Nephite warriors a short distance away, then fixed his gaze on their captain, a man named Moroni. Despite his fear, Lehonti was grateful for the Nephite captain's merciful offer, which had been repeated by the young soldier with the scalp.

Gathering his courage and not looking at his captain, Lehonti stepped forward and laid his weapons at the feet of his conquerors. With a fist to his chest and eyes on the Moroni, he swore an oath of peace—he would never again come to war against the Nephites.

Out of the thousands of Lamanites who had left their homes to fight, Lehonti was one of a much smaller number who returned—each having made a covenant of peace.[2]

Seven months later[3] . . .

A young Lamanite scrambled across the threshold of Lehonti's hut in terror. Lehonti followed on his heels, his fist raised high and his expression set in fierce determination.

"You tell the king I refuse!" Lehonti bellowed as the young man fled through the village for the safety of the trees. "I will *not* go to battle against the Nephites!" But the messenger had already disappeared into the forest near the edge of the village.

Lehonti stared at the tree line for a moment longer then sighed and turned back to his hut. He no longer felt like eating, but he pulled the dish of cassava toward him anyway and picked at the roasted tubers. He had known a summons like this was imminent. The king's messengers had visited many of his brethren already—but, to Lehonti's relief, most had responded with the same staunch refusal.[4]

"I will keep my oath," he muttered softly. His thoughts turned back to the day of the Nephites' crushing defeat at the River Sidon.[5] Sometimes he still dreamed of the battle cries—and the bodies. Not even a year had passed since then, and already the king was anxious to challenge his enemy again.

Lehonti shook his head, certain it had something to do with the Nephite dissenter who had recently joined his people. *Amalickiah.* After failing to make himself king over his own land, Amalickiah had fled for his life to the land of the Lamanites. There, his lust for revenge had festered like a disease, infecting even the king with his malice.

Nephi •

Lamanites led by Amalickiah

Lehonti

Mount Anitpus

Not much time passed before Lehonti had reason to fear the name of Amalickiah. A rumor began to spread that the king had placed Amalickiah in charge of what military forces were still loyal to the crown. His mission? To compel those who would not fight to take up their weapons and go to war.

"Lehonti! I have word!" shouted a young warrior who had just entered the village. He swallowed hard and glanced about as the crowd grew around him, all waiting to hear his news. Lehonti stood tall in their midst.

"The king has gathered those who are loyal to him," the warrior began. "They are led by the dog Amalickiah." He spat the Nephite's name.

"What is that to us?" Lehonti asked, taking a step forward.

"Amalickiah's orders are not to lead the army against the Nephites—at least not yet." He spoke with increasing urgency in his voice. "Lehonti, they are coming for us! Whether to compel us to fight or to destroy us I do not know, but they are coming!"

The crowd had grown silent. The king would not attack his own people ... would he? The unspoken question hung in the air as the people all slowly turned to Lehonti for guidance.

"Let them come," Lehonti said firmly. He turned to face all who had gathered around him. "Spread the word to all who are with us that we will meet in Oneida. There we will make our defense on Mount Antipus. Go!"

Amalickaih

For weeks,[6] men poured in from all areas of the kingdom. Lehonti—who was chosen as their king and leader—organized and prepared them for battle, establishing a stronghold atop Mount Antipus. Spirits were high, and Lehonti felt confident that his men would prevail. How could they not? They were loyal and strong, they outnumbered Amalickiah's army in both manpower and weaponry,[7] and they had the clear tactical advantage. Or they would have, if Amalickiah had had any plans to fight . . .

"Lehonti!" shouted a voice from the darkness at the camp's border. A moment later, several of Lehonti's scouts emerged from the brush, dragging three men toward the light of the fire. "We found them lurking near the mountain pass. They're unarmed and claim to have a message for you."

Lehonti stood slowly. He did not fear these men. He nodded at his scouts to loose them, and the captured men knelt before him. One of them lifted his head and spoke. "Greetings, great king. My master, Amalickiah, wishes an audience with you. Will you come down with us to the foot of the mountain?"

Lehonti laughed out loud. "Your master thinks me a fool," he said. He bent down until he met the man's eyes. "You tell Amalickiah that we will not be forced to go to war against the Nephites. You understand?"

Amalickiah's servants nodded obediently and were released to return and relay Lehonti's message. However, it was not long before they returned, explaining again that Amalickiah urgently desired to meet with the king. Lehonti scorned them, and they departed. A short time later, they returned a third time. He sent them away again, his anger rising. Going down to the foot of the mountain and giving up the security and tactical advantage he held would be utter foolishness.

When Amalickiah's embassy arrived in camp for the fourth time, Lehonti's patience was at an end.

"Do not come here again!" Lehonti grabbed the nearest man's tunic, pulling him in close before shouting in his face, "I will never come down!" He shoved the man back against his brethren. The men shrank before Lehonti, but their expressions remained strangely calm.

"There is no need for anger, great lord," one of the servants said soothingly. "Our master, Amalickiah, has come to you. He is only a short distance from your camp. You need not leave the mountain. You may even bring your guards with you." A second man added, "Please, my lord. It is not far, and what our master has to say is of great importance. Will you not bring your guards and come down a little?"

Lehonti studied the guards in front of him and considered the messenger's words. What was the harm in venturing only a short distance from camp in the company of his guard? Perhaps it would be wise to hear Amalickiah's message. The Nephite had, after all, placed himself in harm's way to deliver it.

"I will go down and hear his words," Lehonti said finally. He turned and sent for his guard.

The servants had spoken truthfully. A short distance from the camp, Amalickiah emerged from the shadow of the trees and stood before Lehonti.

"Most noble Lehonti, hear my words. Our great king has commanded me to compel you and your people to arms," Amalickiah began, his eyes filled with apparent sincerity. "But I do not desire to do this. I desire to unite our forces under your banner." He lowered his voice conspiratorially. "I propose that you come down this very night with your men and surround us while we sleep in our camp. Then I shall surrender to you, giving you command of the whole army."

At first Lehonti said nothing. He watched Amalickiah for a time and then asked, "You would not make this offer unless you stood to gain by it. What is it you want?"

"Only to serve you, great lord." Amalickiah bowed slightly. "Make me your second in command. That is all I ask. I would sooner share in the glory of a mighty army than be leader of a doomed host."

Lehonti hesitated. Amalickiah's plan made sense—and it would put Lehonti in command of the entire Lamanite army. His people would no longer be compelled to attack the Nephites. They would no longer be subject to the whims of the king. This plan would save the lives of countless men. Slowly, Lehonti extended his hand. "I accept."

The plan was put into action just as Amalickiah had proposed. In the light of the early morning, Amalickiah's men awoke, surrounded by a much larger army and completely unprepared to fight. Just as Amalickiah predicted, his men pleaded with him to surrender so that they might save their lives and join Lehonti's forces. Their desire was granted, and Amalickiah became second in command over the entire army. Everything had gone as planned, and Lehonti rejoiced that he had come down to hear the words of Amalickiah that night. Unfortunately for Lehonti, being second in command was not Amalickiah's end goal.

As Amalickiah lay in his tent in the dead of night, his tent flap opened, revealing the face of one of his trusted servants. The man nodded, then quickly stepped inside as Amalickiah rose from his bed. He handed the servant a small vial, his mouth twisted in a tight smile, his eyes narrow and cold.

"Remember what I have told you. Not all at once, but by degrees. Administer it a little at a time."

Over the following weeks, Lehonti's health began to rapidly decline. Even though he was attended to by Amalickiah's most trusted servant, it was not long before he lay at the point of death. Knowing he did not have long to live, he called for the man he thought was his friend to give him comfort in his last hours.

Amalickiah entered the tent and dismissed the servant so that he alone sat with Lehonti. Then, leaning close to Lehonti's frail form, he began to laugh softly.

Lehonti's eyes opened wide in confusion and then fear as Amalickiah began to speak.

"I never could have beaten you in a fair fight. You would not even

come down from your mountain—not all the way, anyway." Amalickiah's twisted grin grew wider. "But you would come down a little, and then I brought you all the way down myself. When I gave you my army, I earned your trust." Amalickiah leaned in, patting Lehonti's face, as if consoling him. "But from the moment you held conference with me, you were in my power.[8]

Amalickiah straightened up and smiled. "Of course, I could have poisoned you all at once, but I've learned my lesson well. A little at a time is far more effective—and far less suspicious. You are nothing now. *I* command your forces, and soon *I* will be *king!*"

Lehonti's eyes darted about as if to find some help or escape. His labored breathing came in short gasps, and he began to tremble. He looked pleadingly at his murderer but found no mercy there.

"And when I am king," Amalickiah continued, bringing his mouth close to the dying man's ear, "I will wage a war with the Nephites unlike any that this land has ever known."

Lehonti lurched forward but managed only to cast himself to the ground, where he lay still, his eyes frozen in horror, his last breath slowly escaping with a hiss.

After Lehonti's death, Amalickiah became the leader of the entire Lamanite army. He then traveled back to the capital city of Nephi, where he would put into effect his treacherous plans to become the king of all the Lamanites—but that's another story.

Endnotes

1 There is actually no direct information linking Lehonti to those warriors who were led by Zerahemnah to battle against the Nephites in Alma 43–44, but I have reason to believe that he may have been. It is interesting to note that in a

matter of months, many Lamanites rebelled against their king's order to return against the Nephites to war and that the rebels appointed Lehonti to be their king. I think he must have had some credentials. I suspect he was a warrior of some experience, skill, and honor. Why would Lehonti risk the wrath of the Lamanite king by refusing to go to war? Could it be that he had made an oath he would not break?

2   Alma 43–44 but, particularly, 44:13–5. For the purpose of brevity, I did not mention the fact that although many Lamanites initially entered into a covenant of peace, Zerahemnah and a remnant of his men refused and continued in their bloody battle with Moroni before they eventually surrendered and pled for mercy (Alma 44:16–20).

3   Seven months is an estimate. We know that the surrender of Zerahemnah and his army ended the eighteenth year (Alma 44:24). So Amalickiah rose up against the Nephites, was defeated by Captain Moroni, fled to the Lamanites lands, befriended the Lamanite king, defeated Lehonti, killed the king, and became king himself—all before the "latter end" of the nineteenth year (Alma 46–48:2). Amalickiah had a busy year.

4   There is no direct discussion of why the Lamanites did not want to go to battle, other than the note that they feared the Nephites (Alma 47:2). But I still believe the warriors' oath to Captain Moroni must have played a part in this rebellion (Alma 44:15, 20). At no other time do the Lamanites so blatantly disobey an order from their king. The fact that so many of them are willing to face the king's wrath rather than go to war leads me to believe that at least some of them are honoring their oath of peace made only months before.

5   Alma 43–44.

6   This time frame is just an estimate based on the idea that the events described in Alma 47 took a matter of months to unfold. I don't know how long it took to gather everyone together, but I don't think it could have taken too long.

7   It is interesting to note that the Lamanites identify Onidah as "a place of arms" (Alma 47:5). Some, most notably John L. Sorenson in *An Ancient American Setting for the Book of Mormon*, have speculated that this indicates a location where supplies were plentiful for creating weapons, such as an obsidian outcropping (Salt Lake City: Deseret Book and FARMS, 1985, 252).

8   The spiritual lessons from this story are well described in an insightful talk from Elder Robert D. Hales of the Quorum of the Twelve Apostles in a CES Fireside for Young Adults, which was given on March 1, 2009, at Brigham Young University. It is currently available to read and download at www.lds.org.

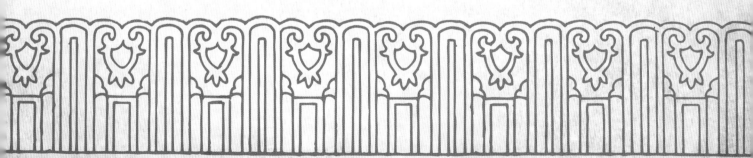

*F*ramed for a murder he did not commit, he must find a new home in the nation that was once his bitter enemy, finding redemption and becoming a hero.

14 *L*aman

Hero of the Nephites and Lamanites

*A*lma 47, 55

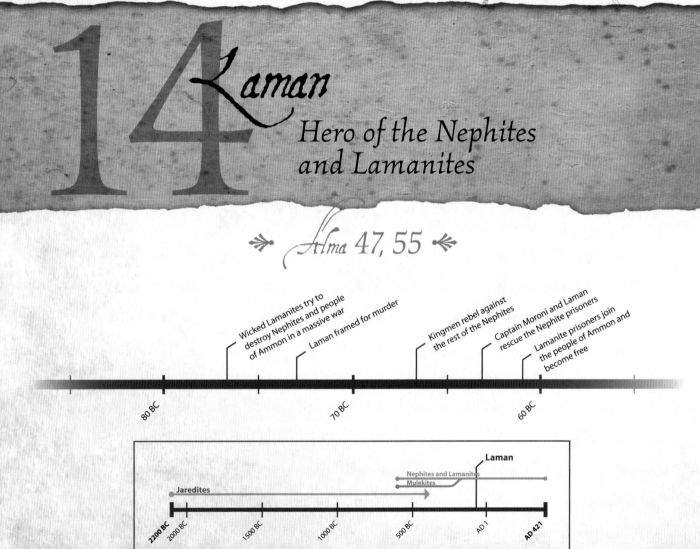

Wicked Lamanites try to destroy Nephites and people of Ammon in a massive war

Laman framed for murder

Kingmen rebel against the rest of the Nephites

Captain Moroni and Laman rescue the Nephite prisoners

Lamanite prisoners join the people of Ammon and become free

80 BC   70 BC   60 BC

Laman

Nephites and Lamanites
Mulekites

Jaredites

2200 BC 2000 BC   1500 BC   1000 BC   500 BC   AD 1   AD 421

The sun was high above the eastern sea and the Nephite military camp was alive with the murmur of activity. Thousands of warriors were practicing drills, and cooks were hauling water for the evening meal. Armorers worked stone and metal, wood and hide, and messengers carried commands between the various divisions. The flap of the chief captain's tent flew open suddenly, and all activity ceased. Moroni was enraged and the poor Lamanite messenger who had just delivered an epistle retreated slowly behind him.

Captain Moroni was an imposing man and a powerful warrior. He was also a mighty man of God, and his next words carried a fierce power that disquieted even the war-hardened Lamanite messenger.

"Your master, Ammoron, knows that his cause for coming to war against us is only a pretense for his own greed. This war, which his wretched brother Amalickiah began, and which he continues, is unjust, and this very epistle from your master confirms it!" He reached forward and grabbed the messenger, holding him fast with his powerful hands. "I will not exchange prisoners with Ammoron! I will not grant unto your master more power than he has already!" Captain Moroni stared into the man's eyes and emphasized each word he spoke. "As Ammoron would not grant unto me mine epistle, behold, I will give unto him according to my words; yea, I will *seek death* among them until they shall sue for peace!"

Moroni paused for a moment to let his promise sink into the heart of the Lamanite, and then he released him. The Lamanite slumped part way to the ground, as if his legs no longer had strength to stand. Moroni returned to his tent, and the dazed messenger was escorted out of the camp. The men of the army of Moroni stared silently at Moroni's tent and then glanced at each other, dumbfounded. They had never seen their captain in such a temperament before. Moroni was known for his compassion and mercy on the field of battle. Many times he had allowed his enemies to return to their homes in peace after covenanting with an oath that they would not return again to war against the Nephites, but now . . .

Moroni's words, "I will seek death among them until they shall sue for peace," quickly circulated around the camp from division to division until they reached the ears of a mighty warrior who was distinctive among the Nephite armies of Moroni. The warrior's name was Laman, and he was a Lamanite.

Rewrapping the handle of his sword with a strip of thick hide, he responded without looking up to the soldier who'd passed along Moroni's words. "So the time for mercy has passed. This is grave news indeed."

Laman was well liked and admired for his prowess as a warrior. Despite his heritage, he had lived among the Nephites for the last nine years and had served in the military nearly half of that time. Why he left the Lamanites was the subject of many rumors. Laman himself did not like to talk about his former life, but no one doubted his loyalty to the Nephites, and many men already owed their lives to him for his heroic acts on the battlefield.

Strapping his sword over his shoulder, Laman prepared to retire to his tent, his heart heavy with the meaning of Moroni's words. Just as he had begun to leave, his captain marched into camp and called out to him.

"Laman, Captain Moroni is looking for a very special kind of man for an important mission. I told him to look no further, because I had just the man for him."

"Why?" Laman responded, curious about why he'd been singled out. "What kind of man is he looking for?"

"A Lamanite," the captain replied with a smile. "Come. Captain Moroni is waiting for you."

When Laman entered the chief captain's tent, he was immediately and warmly greeted by the legendary leader.

"I am told you have distinguished yourself among my ranks for your skill in battle and your loyalty to our nation," Moroni began.

Laman nodded, unsure how else to respond. "It is an honor to serve my nation."

"Please, sit with me," Moroni continued, gesturing to some mats on one side of the large tent. "I have a mission that is of the greatest importance. I fear it can only be successful with your help."

Laman wondered why his orders were being approached so cautiously. "You have but to command, and it will be done."

Captain Moroni stared at Laman for a moment before continuing. "Why do you fight with us and against the nation of your birth?"

Laman was surprised by the question. "I have joined the people of Nephi just as the people of Ammon have. I am no different."

"The people of Ammon have entered into a covenant with God never to shed the blood of any man. They do not fight with us. Instead they help to support our armies with their substance. And so I ask again, why do you fight with us?" Moroni's words were calm, but it was clear he wanted an answer that Laman was reluctant to give.

The tent remained silent while Laman worked up the courage to tell his story. He then unraveled the memories that he had long since tried to bury.

"I was always taught to hate your people," Laman began, not meeting the captain's eyes. "When the sons of Mosiah came, I would not listen to their message about the Nephite God, and I hated all those who did. When the converts, including our king, eventually left to live among the Nephites, I was among the warriors that followed them and sought their destruction. I fought valiantly against your people in the horrific war that followed." His voice had grown quiet, but he continued his history. "Because of my prowess, I was chosen as a guard for the new king of the Lamanites, and for five years I served him faithfully. This was a high honor for me, and it brought respect to my family."[1]

Laman finally looked up into the eyes of his great captain. "And then Amalickiah came into our land."

The Lamanite capital of Nephi, nine years earlier.

A servant hurried forward and bowed before the mighty king of the vast Lamanite nation. The king raised him up with a motion of his hand, and the servant arose.

"They are here, my lord! Amalickiah has done it."

The king hurried to the steps of the grand palace with the members of his elite guard. There he could observe, past the sea of onlookers, a massive force of men marching toward the city. *My men.* The king smiled. *My men who will destroy the people of Nephi.* He smiled with joy and waited anxiously to receive Amalickiah's embassy.

Laman, one of the king's guards, was also anxious—but for a different reason. He had been charged to protect the king from unseen danger, and Amalickiah seemed too good to be true. He had come to them as a fugitive from the Nephites. He would have become king in his own land, or so he told them, but a rebellion of the government against him had sent him into exile. No one could question the veracity of his story. In less than a year among the Lamanites, he had gained the trust of the king and had been given the task of uniting the armies of the land under one banner to begin a war against the Nephites. He had miraculously succeeded and now stood in front of a massive host of Lamanite warriors as they moved toward the palace. It was an awesome sight, but it was also a little . . . unnerving.

The Lamanite king now stood ready to receive the Nephite's embassy. Laman and the other guards stood behind him, an ominous presence. Even though the approaching servants of Amalickiah had proven their loyalty by accomplishing the will of the king, Laman was ever watchful and wary.

The servants' manners were flawless. They did not approach the king but knelt before him with great reverence. Laman was a bit surprised at such a sincere sign of respect from Nephites that had only recently been welcomed among his people. The king stepped forward and extended his hand to raise the servants up. The first servant arose, and it was only then that Laman saw it—the look in the servant's eye betrayed him. Even the king could see it now, but it was too late. The servant struck with deadly accuracy as he stabbed the king to the heart. Laman froze with shock. He had failed. The king was dead!

Laman   167

Laman and the other guards stepped forward to avenge their fallen king but then stopped. Something was wrong. The servants of Amalickiah didn't flee. They didn't even move. They stood there defiantly. It was then Laman realized that the power of the kingdom had shifted. Even now Amalickiah and a contingent of warriors were ascending the palace steps. The Lamanites would have a new king, and those loyal to the old regime would not be tolerated. Amalickiah had the support of the entire Lamanite army. He had all the power he needed. How Amalickiah would cover up the king's murder, Laman did not know, but he quickly understood one thing. They had to run—now!

Laman could not imagine feeling more shame than he did as he and the other guards turned from the body of the king they had sworn to protect and fled. Thoughts filled Laman's mind as they ran. *Perhaps we can tell others what happened and raise a force of those loyal to the king to fight against this usurper of the throne. There are many who loved the king . . . surely they will rise up to avenge him! Amalickiah will regret the day he challenged us—the servants of the rightful king.*

But then, through the halls of the palace, words echoed that struck each man like a knife to the heart and stripped them of their hope—words that would make them enemies to all who had once admired and trusted them:

"Behold, the servants of the king have stabbed him to the heart, and he has fallen and they have fled; behold, come and see."

Then they heard in the distance the shout of Amalickiah, filled with mock despair: "Whosoever loved the king, let him go forth, and pursue his servants that they may be slain!"

Laman and the other guards were now completely condemned. They could not return home, and there was no place for them to hide in all the land of the Lamanites. All was truly lost. In their hopeless despair, they fled northward into the wilderness.

The captain's tent was silent for a moment, except for the stylus of the scribe who was making careful notes of Laman's account for the records of the Nephites. "So you eventually reached the land of Melek and joined the people of Ammon?"

Laman nodded.

Moroni sat forward. "You now had to throw yourselves at the mercy of the very people you had tried to slaughter only a few years before, in the heart of the very nation you had warred against?"

Laman smiled slightly at an irony that he had considered many times over the years, and he nodded.

"And how were you received by the people of Ammon?" Moroni asked with a glint in his eyes. "Did these converted Lamanites, these 'enemies,' take you in?"

"Enemies?" Laman's thoughts reached back. "There was a time when I would have described them as such, but now they are my people . . . my family . . . my saviors. When we had nothing, they took my brethren and me in. They knew who we were. They had every right to hate us." Laman's voice suddenly got quieter, more reverent, as he spoke. "But they showed us such love. They helped us build a life among them, and we listened to their teachings of God. The message was suddenly so sweet. It wasn't long before we became their brothers in Christ."[2]

Moroni allowed a small, knowing smile to flicker across his face. *Of course, that is what the people of Ammon would do*, he thought to himself.

"I lived with them for the next five years,"[3] Laman continued enjoying the sweet memories. "We received word of Amalickiah's monumental failure when attacking the Nephites at the city of Noah.[4] I was delighted that he could not prevail against my new people, but I wondered what treachery he would try next. I soon put these thoughts in the   back   of my mind, however. I enjoyed incredible peace in my new life. Many said that we lived among the Nephites at a time when they had not known such happiness since the days of Nephi.[5] The people were prosperous and peaceful, but none more so than the people of Ammon. My brethren were distinguished for their zeal in serving God and men. They were perfectly honest in everything they did, and they were unshakably firm in the faith of Christ.[6] I was certain I had found paradise." Laman closed his eyes briefly; the joyful memories had come to an end.

"Perhaps I was a fool to think it could last." He looked up at Moroni. "You know better than anyone else the events that shook the Nephites after the death of our chief judge, Nephihah. Pahoran was chosen by the voice of the people, but men inspired by the same lust for power as Amalickiah challenged Pahoran's right to the judgment seat. These 'king-men' sought to throw down the free government. They desired to wield absolute power and authority over the people. I thank my God that Pahoran retained the judgement seat and the free government was preserved. But, as you well know, the king-men did not fade away. They sulked and waited, watching for another opportunity to weaken the reign of the judges.

"I began to see a danger I had been unable fight in my old homeland manifest itself once again. Amalickiah's greed and pride had destroyed my life among my former people, and I could see that same plague beginning to unfold in my new home, among a people I had come to love.

"Then Amalickiah returned with a mighty force of Lamanites and began a march on the fortified cities along the eastern coast, and when he began to have success, thousands of the king-men rebelled against our nation and refused to defend it.

Then you threw down the rebellion and raised the Title of Liberty again to inspire the people to action."

"And that is when you joined our ranks?" Moroni asked, fascinated by Laman's journey.

"I knew thousands among the Nephites had been killed putting down the king-men, and Amalickiah had taken seven heavily fortified cities[7] along the coastline and entrenched himself in our land.[8] I could see that new troops were desperately needed."

"But the people of Ammon are not required to fight because of the oath they've made to God," Moroni coaxed. "No one would have expected you to break with their traditions. So, I ask you again, why fight with us?"

Laman had fire in his eyes when he looked at Moroni. "I *will not* let Amalickiah or any other power-hungry men destroy my new home or tear down our government!" Laman cried out, rising to his feet, unable to sit still anymore. "Not this time! I will stand and fight for our God, our religion, our freedom, and our peace!"

Moroni allowed himself another brief smile of satisfaction. That was the very answer he had been hoping for. He wasted no time filling Laman in on the details of his plan.

"You have fought with us for the last four years. Amalickiah has been slain, but his brother Ammoron carries on this cursed war. The Lamanites had captured many Nephites—men, women, and children. Their safety weighs heavily on my mind. I will no longer negotiate with Ammoron. I know that the prisoners are kept in the fortified city of Gid, and I will need your help to free them."

When the chief captain had finished laying out his plan, Laman asked, "And when the guards are disabled, shall we slay them?"

Moroni looked at him seriously, "Not unless you must. God willing, we will rescue them all without the shedding of blood."

The time for mercy has not passed, Laman thought, and he smiled.

That night Laman and a small team of his men found themselves in sight of the city of Gid. He quietly handed out the weapons that captain Moroni had prepared for them.

"What is this?" one of the men asked in a low whisper.

"Wine," Laman whispered back with a smile. "Strong wine. Come on."

Laman saw the fires burning as the guards kept watch. Laman did not hesitate. He boldly walked toward them, almost enthusiastically. His men followed behind.

"Hold there! Who approaches?" called out one of the Lamanite guards.

"Fear not!" Laman responded, sounding a bit out of breath as if he had been running. "I am a Lamanite. Behold, we have escaped from the Nephites, and they sleep; and behold . . ." Laman showed them the flasks, and his voice became almost musical, "we have taken of their wine and brought with us."

As Laman and his men entered the circle of firelight, the guards could see that he was in fact a Lamanite. Their eyes didn't rest on him long, however, once they'd seen the flasks of wine.

"Give us of your wine, that we may drink," one of the guards said enthusiastically, moving aside to make room for the new arrivals. "We are glad that ye have thus taken wine with you for we are weary."

Laman became grave and serious, trying to sound responsible. "Let us keep of our wine till we go against the Nephites to battle." He made as if to find someplace to stash the wine for later use.

The first guard, now sounding a little desperate, pleaded, "We are weary." He sidled next to Laman and spoke almost as if it was just the two of them. "Let us take of the wine, and by and by we shall receive wine for our rations, which will strengthen us to go against the Nephites."

This met with joyous approval all around. Laman pretended to think about it for a moment, and then he let a smile slowly spread across his face. "You may do according to your desires." Laman spoke these words as if he had been convinced of something he wanted to do anyway—which, of course, he was.

With much cheering the flasks were opened and the wine shared. All shared their compliments for the delicious taste of the wine and the generosity of Laman and his men. It was remarkable how quickly they finished the wine, and it was even more amazing how soon they were all asleep—deeply asleep.

Laman and his men quickly returned to the camp of Moroni, where the chief captain put the next phase of his plan in action. Men of Moroni, laden with weapons, silently transported weapons into the city and armed all the men, women, and children who were prisoners there. Then all the soldiers of Moroni, including Laman, surrounded the city and waited for the sun to rise.

They waited in great anticipation, but when the sun rose, it took some time before the Lamanites began to stir. The guard who awoke first became groggily aware of the predicament they were in,

and he woke the others. The Lamanite captains awoke to find themselves surrounded by armed Nephite warriors. There was no refuge in their city either, for all the prisoners stood, weapons in hand, ready for conflict. The captains hung their heads in defeat. The Lamanite captains came forward, dropped their weapons at the feet of Moroni, and pleaded for mercy.

As they awaited their reply from the mighty Nephite captain, they chanced to notice the Lamanite who had, the night before, given them the wine. He was smiling at them, but it was not a glib or arrogant smile. This smile was ... loving. It said to them, *Welcome, brothers. You are no longer under the thumb of the wicked tyrants that you have suffered with for the last nine years. Witness the nature of the people I have joined. See the mercy that their God teaches them.*

The mercy the Lamanite captains had pled for was granted. Moroni accepted their surrender and took them all as prisoners of the Nephites.

The Nephites who had formerly been prisoners expressed their gratitude to Moroni and his men for their rescue. Laman was hailed, by soldier and rescued family alike, for his bravery and loyalty to the cause of freedom. The Lamanite guards also slowly realized that Laman had been a hero to them too. Laman and the other Nephites could easily have butchered them in their drunken sleep, but they'd let them live. Why? It was a question that they would each ponder in their hearts over the next two years while they remained prisoners of the Nephites.

The Nephite men who had been imprisoned joined the forces of captain Moroni and were a great strength to his army. The Lamanite guards were eventually taken to the city of Bountiful where the Nephites kept their prisoners heavily guarded. Laman continued to serve in the forces of captain Moroni, but the record is silent as to whether or not he survived to see the end of the war. He may have lived to return to his home and friends in Melek. He also may have given his life in the service of his new people. This much we know—his courage and willingness to serve saved the lives of many Nephites.

But whatever happened to the Lamanite guards whose lives Laman was instrumental in saving? Two years later, shortly before the war ended, Lamanite prisoners expressed a desire to lay down their weapons of war and join the people of Ammon. Even though battles with the Lamanite army continued to rage, the Nephites granted this wish to as many Lamanite prisoners as desired it. The Lamanite men who Laman had helped to preserve at the city of Gid were among those who moved to Melek and joined the people of Ammon. In fact, all Lamanite prisoners made this choice.[9] They began to work the land of their new home, growing crops and raising flocks. They heard the word of the Lord from those who had once been their brothers and now were again[10]—but that's another story.

Endnotes

1 Laman's backstory comes from the few clues we are given in the scriptures. When the king of all the Lamanites, Anti-Nephi-Lehi, left with the other converts to live with the Nephites (Alma 27), the Lamanite nation had to restructure its government. A new king was chosen and with him guards and servants. If I were king, I would choose guards from my very best warriors. How would I know of a warrior's skills unless he had proved himself in battle? If the new Lamanite king also thought this way, he would have chosen from those who fought in the great battle described in Alma 28:1–2.

2 There is no direct evidence to indicate that Laman and his fellow guards became Christians, but I have a hard time imagining these men could have lived among the people of Ammon and constantly seen their testimonies alive in their hearts without being touched by the Spirit.

3 72 B.C. (Alma 46:37) to 67 B.C. (Alma 51:1). Although we don't know for sure when Laman joined captain Moroni's army, it seems to me that after the uprising of the king-men and Amalickiah's invasion would be a logical time.

4 When Amalickiah finally became king of the Lamanites and could exact revenge on the Nephites, he immediately sent armies to attack Ammonihah (a city that had previously been easy to overpower). His armies were scared off by the amazing fortifications that Captain Moroni had put into place, so they tried then to attack a neighboring city, Noah. That city proved to be even better fortified than Ammonihah, but they tried to attack it anyway. The Lamanites lost more than one thousand men, whereas the Nephites did not lose one (Alma 49:1–25). Take that, Amalickiah!

5 Alma 50:23.

6 Alma 27:27.

7 The seven cities were Moroni, Nephihah, Lehi, Morianton, Omner, Gid, and Mulek (Alma 51:22–26).

8 Alma 51.

9 We know the former guards of Gid joined the people of Ammon because all the Lamanite prisoners did (Alma 62:27–29).

10 If Laman did return home to Melek, imagine what those former guards would have said to the man who helped change their lives. If Laman lost his life and was never able to return, think how great his memory would be in the minds and hearts of those whose lives he had both spiritually and physically saved.

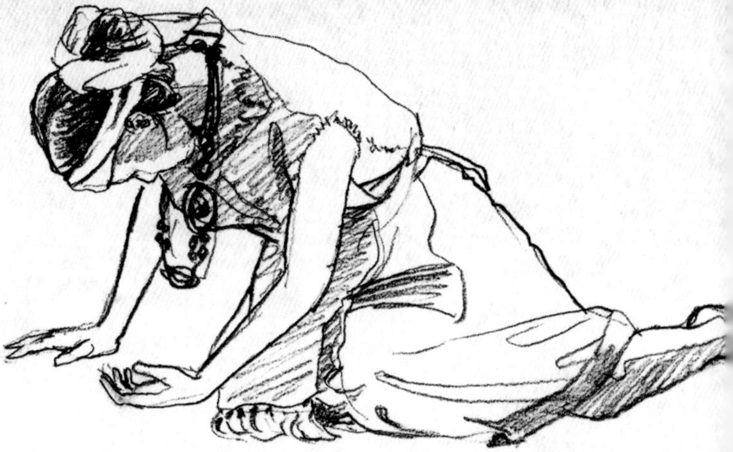

A daring act of treason was underway, and no one could stop it—except for one woman, a most unlikely hero.

15 Morianton's Maidservant

An Unbreakable Spirit

Alma 50

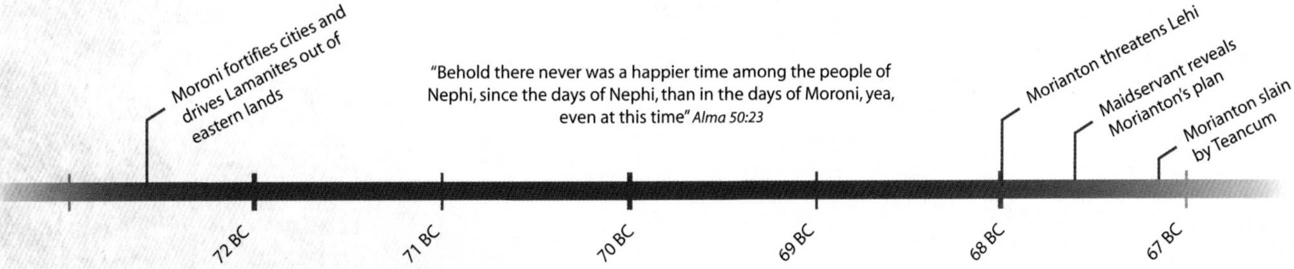

Moroni fortifies cities and drives Lamanites out of eastern lands
"Behold there never was a happier time among the people of Nephi, since the days of Nephi, than in the days of Moroni, yea, even at this time" Alma 50:23
Morianton threatens Lehi
Maidservant reveals Morianton's plan
Morianton slain by Teancum
72 BC
71 BC
70 BC
69 BC
68 BC
67 BC

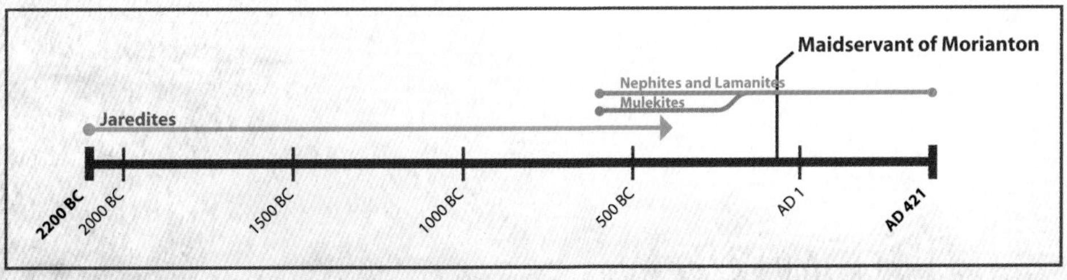

Maidservant of Morianton
Nephites and Lamanites
Mulekites
Jaredites
2200 BC
2000 BC
1500 BC
1000 BC
500 BC
AD 1
AD 421

Sabriah lay in a heap on the floor, sobs wracking her body. She could feel a trickle of blood running down the side of her face, mingling with her tears. Her entire body ached, and the skin on her arms and back felt tender even against the fabric of her clothes. With each heaving breath she took, her ribs seized with pain, yet she couldn't seem to stop weeping. How had she ended up here? Why, with so much happiness and prosperity surrounding her in the land of the Nephites, must she bear so much misery?

"I tell you, the land belongs to *us*." Morianton spoke with such confidence that it would have been impossible to dispute him, had the truth not been so obvious. He sat cross-legged at a short table with his commanders, attended by his servants. Sabriah, a beautiful young woman, stepped back slightly at the dangerous tone in her master's voice. She unconsciously reached up to touch the fading bruise on her face—the hallmark of serving a man with a passionate temper.

Representatives from the land of Lehi sat on the opposite side of the table, none of which were too happy with the tone of Morianton's deliberation. A man with graying hair spoke up. "The borders of our lands have been clearly established. The territory in question is well within the borders of the land of Lehi." His voice belied his frustration that they were still discussing this matter. "How long must we endure this contention you have brought against us?"

Morianton slammed his hands on the table. "Until I am satisfied," he said maliciously.

The old man's voice took on a sharper edge. "We have been more than patient—"

Morianton stood swiftly, upending the table and sending its contents scattering to the ground with a series of crashes. "*I* have been more than patient, and I *demand* that you surrender your claims to that land." His voice dropped, and the knuckles of his hands cracked as he balled them into fists, adding, "Or I will take it by the sword."

"You wouldn't dare," came the quiet voice of the leader of the men of Lehi, who remained seated. Morianton turned to his men, his face burning with rage.

"Prepare the soldiers," he commanded between clenched teeth before turning back to the other men. "I will show you what I dare!"

His servants flinched as he stormed past them and out of the council meeting, but they quietly fell into place behind him, along with his commanders. The men of Lehi simply sat for a few moments, looking around them in bewilderment. Then their leader stood, resolved at what they must do.[1]

"What do you mean they fled?" Morianton asked, looking up from his meal and chewing loudly. A nearby servant hurriedly picked up an empty dish and backed away.

The commander, who was the messenger of the unfavorable news, shook his head. "You know as well as I do that we have no claim to that land.[2] The people of Lehi have fled to the camp of Captain Moroni to appeal to him for assistance." His voice took on an edge of pleading. "We must tell our warriors to stand down. It is the only way to salvage this situation!"

The color drained from Morianton's face at the mention of Moroni's name, and he stopped chewing. "They have fled to Captain Moroni?" Morianton eyes began to twitch as panic slowly gripped him. "We must get out of this land," he said softly. "Moroni will find out the truth, and he will come and destroy us! He will . . ."[3] He stopped short, humiliated by how much fear he could hear in his own voice. He looked up at his manservant, who looked back at him in barely concealed surprise. Morianton's face turned a deep shade of red, and, without warning, he leapt to his feet and threw the man to the ground, dishes and all. "Gather my people," he said to his commander. "I must speak to them." Without a backward glance, he left the room.

Sabriah had hidden behind the door when her master had flown into a rage. She rushed forward now to help her fellow servant to his feet, then helped him pick up the broken pottery and spilled food. This was not the first time she had seen such things. She was both grateful for the man's safety and sickened to know that it could have been much worse. He was lucky.

She shook her head, thinking of the foolish girl she had been when she first arrived. She'd thought herself so honored to be chosen as the maidservant of the lord and master of this land. Her joy had faded far more quickly than the bruises that, from time to time, marked her body. Yet she remained, held by the fear of what might happen if she tried to leave. To flee was a sentence of death. *If I just keep my head low, I should be all right,* she told herself once more.

Morianton stood before the multitude and lifted his arms in the air, crying, "My people! We, in this land, have been maligned. The people of Lehi have lied to Captain Moroni, and he is coming here now to destroy us all." He paused a moment to let his words frighten the people, as they were intended to do. He was pleased when a swell of worried murmurs rose from the assembly. "Rather than fight," he continued. "Let us leave this wicked land and go into the lands northward. There we will find a land of many waters and rich abundance. There we can build a great city and unite with the people of those lands. There we can become our own nation—a great nation where we may do as we please, no longer subjecting ourselves to the rules of this corrupt land. In time this nation will bow before us! Who is with me?"

There was a moment's silence, but then, as the commanders of Morianton began to cheer, others joined in. Soon all were celebrating this new plan. Morianton's tight-lipped grimace grew into a smile, and he extended his hands toward his people.

However, as the people began to disperse to their homes and prepare for travel, his smile faded, and he was once again haunted by humiliation. His plan had worked, but nothing could erase the fact that he was cowering before Captain Moroni like a dog. Then a whisper, floating from somewhere in the crowd, caught Morianton's attention. "Cowardice. That's what it is," the voice said. But when he spun around, all he saw the multitude. It could have been any one of them. Morianton's smile melted back into a snarl, and, fists clenched and shaking, he turned to his house once more.

"My lord, please," Sabriah said cautiously as she approached. "Shall we begin the preparations to flee?"

Though the question was innocently asked, at the word *flee*, Morianton visibly stiffened. He turned toward her, seething, the vein in his forehead bulging.

"Flee?" he whispered. Then he advanced toward her. "*Flee?*" Without another word, he fell upon her like a predator, striking viciously, unleashing his fury and humiliation with every blow. When at last his fists stopped pounding, Sabriah lay on the ground, barely moving. Breathing heavily, Morianton arose and retired to his bed.

Sabriah had no idea how long she lay there in the dark, first simply trying to breath and then sobbing as quietly as her pain and humiliation allowed. With every sob she feared that he would return and beat her again. After what felt like hours, she slowly tried to move. She could barely raise herself up with her hands. Her head was swimming, and her stomach lurched with every movement.

When she finally managed to get to a kneeling position, Sabriah began the arduous task of crawling toward the servants' quarters. Then she stopped. Why should she return to her quarters? The fear and shame she felt began to harden into anger. *I should leave this place and tell the Nephite captains what my master is doing.* She could put a stop to Morianton's treachery and end his tyranny. Slowly the icy hand of fear crept back, and, in the darkness of the corridor, it seemed an impossible task.

She dismissed her plan and continued to make her way slowly toward the servants' quarters. She told herself that in the morning she would be able to see matters more clearly. Everything would be back to normal tomorrow, and her wounds would heal . . . until it happened again.

But it would be madness to leave. Sabriah hung her head as she continued her slow crawl down the corridor. *What about stopping Morianton?* a little voice inside her persisted. She shook her head slightly again. That was the work of warriors. She was a maidservant. Yet . . . not one of the Nephite captains knew what her master was planning. Otherwise they would stop Morianton, ensuring that no one else would be hurt because of his greed and lust for power. She and the other servants would be rid of him, and the Nephite nation would be assured of peace. *If they only knew his plans.*

Dizzy waves washed over her. If she left, Morianton would send men to hunt her down and kill her. She knew his plans. He wouldn't think twice about making sure his secrets never left her lips.

As she tried to stand, the room began to spin, and she collapsed to the ground.

When Sabriah awoke some time later her body still ached terribly, but her mind was clearer. If she allowed herself to be taken to the lands northward with Morianton, she would never escape. She was certain of it. She thought of the mighty Nephite captains. She knew the stories of Captain Moroni; she knew he'd dedicated his life to protect his people. He had hoisted banners throughout the land and inspired the people to defend their God, their religion, their freedom, and their peace.[4] Morianton would destroy that peace if the people did nothing to stop him—if *she* did nothing to stop him.

Sabriah listened for any sign of movement, but the house was still dark and quiet. She took a deep breath, feeling strengthened somehow as she thought of the words she had seen on Moroni's banners. With some effort, she stood and pulled the hair back from her face. Then she made her way carefully through the house and into the night, walking as quickly as she dared toward the land of Jershon, where Captain Moroni was encamped.

At first she journeyed on the main roads, but once the first rays of sunlight appeared over the horizon, she hid in the cover of the trees, making her travel much slower. Once dawn broke, Morianton would discover her missing, and she was certain that he would send men after her. It was difficult enough to make her way through the abundant wilderness, her body throbbing with pain, but she was also burdened by the relentless fear that Morianton's men would find her.

She was able to find some water as she traveled, but she had brought no food, and her body began to weaken from hunger and fatigue. When night fell, she collapsed from exhaustion and allowed herself a few moments' rest before fear brought her back to her feet.

When she finally reached the camp of Moroni[5] in the land of Jershon, she fell to the ground. Sabriah had imagined herself being confident and strong before the men of Moroni, but when they came to her aid, she could only drop her head in her arms as she lay on the ground and sobbed with relief. Morianton could never reach her here.

As she began to regain control of her emotions, she heard other footsteps running toward her. She wiped her eyes and looked up. She was surrounded by strong young men whose expressions bespoke compassion. They were asking where she had come from and what had happened to her. But before she could reply, two men broke the circle and knelt beside her. One of the men knelt next to her and gently placed a hand on her shoulder. The other man offered his arm, helping her sit up. There was no mistaking who he was—Captain Moroni.

"Get water, quickly! And my healer!" Moroni called to his men after seeing the condition of the young woman in front of him. The man who had helped her sit up quickly unslung a water flask from his shoulders and held it out for her to drink. Sabriah drank deeply to satisfy her thirst, then she looked into the eyes of the chief captain and delivered the message she had suffered so much to bring.

"Morianton," she said urgently. "He is leading his people to the land northward to begin a new nation."

Captain Moroni paused, surprised. "Where did you hear this?" he inquired cautiously.

"From his own lips," Sabriah replied. She lowered her eyes. "I was a servant in his house."

The captain was silent for a time as he considered the weight of this news. The men who had gathered to hear Sabriah's story glanced at one another in silence.

The man behind Sabriah gently lowered her to the ground, resting her head on his own loosely folded cloak. Then he turned to his captain. "If he takes the narrow pass . . ."

"I know, Teancum," Moroni replied gravely. "The narrow pass is easy to defend, and we would needlessly lose many men trying to reclaim it."

"If we even *could* reclaim it," Teancum replied with a look of uncertainty.

Captain Moroni thought for a moment and then said, "If a man like Morianton reached the lands northward, it would bring serious consequences to our people. We would soon find ourselves threatened by Lamanites to the south and a new enemy to the north—a well-fortified enemy because of the narrow pass.[6] This would surely lead to the overthrow of our liberty and peace." He gave each of the men a meaningful look. "We must not let that happen."

Moroni turned again to Teancum. "Take your men and stop the flight of Morianton into the land northward."

Teancum nodded and shouted instructions to the men around him, who quickly left to prepare for the journey. After they were gone, Sabriah lifted herself up slightly to give Teancum back his cloak. When she held it out to him, he knelt beside her again and said in a low voice, "I know the marks of a fist, but I have never seen them worn by a woman. Not like this. Who has done this to you?"

- **Morianton**
- **Morianton's maidservant**
- **Teancum and his soldiers**

"My master, Morianton," she said quietly, her voice trembling as she said his name.

Teancum's eyes narrowed, and the muscles in his jaw clenched. He nodded somberly to the young woman and then departed to gather his men. Sabriah was carefully transported to a nearby tent, where her injuries were tended to. The military camp was well equipped to treat her battered body, and soon her wounds had been washed and her broken bones set. In time she was nourished back to health.

The people rejoiced when Teancum returned with news of a successful mission. He had overtaken Morianton by the narrow pass, just as Sabriah had indicated he would. Although Teancum offered a peaceful resolution, the people of Morianton were so stubborn—inspired as they were by Morianton's wickedness and flattering words—that a battle commenced. Captain Teancum's warriors, superior in strength and aided by the Lord, quickly defeated Morianton's army. Morianton himself had come face to face with Captain Teancum and did not survive the encounter.

Stories of Sabriah's courage quickly spread among the Nephites. Her honorable service was even engraved in the record of the kings, on the plates of Nephi.[7] The record told of her resolute bravery, of how a major peril was averted, and of how peace was maintained in the land—all because a valiant young woman, battered but not broken, risked everything to do what was right.

Often it is that wicked men like Morianton must be removed before peace can be restored in the land. Sometimes, however, the Lord, who knows all men's hearts, may call upon a longtime enemy of righteousness to do a great work for Him—but that's another story.

Endnotes

1 Alma 50:26.

2 Alma 50:27.

3 It is unclear what Captain Moroni would actually have done, but it is clear what Morianton thought would happen to him (Alma 50:28).

4 Alma 46:12, 36.

5 We have no indication of how long it took for her to get to the land of Jershon, but it may have been days.

6 Alma 50:1–11. The narrow pass and the lands northward were of such strategic importance that time and time again the Nephites allotted significant resources to defending them. In the whole history of the Book of Mormon, the only time they lose control of these areas is in the days of Mormon, when the Nephite nation is nearing its end.

7 Please note that the maidservant's name is fictional in this book. We only have an abridged record of this account. I wonder if more of this maidservant's story was written in the full account on the large plates of Nephi. That would have been quite an honor.

In the days of the most powerful missionaries the Nephites had ever seen, the Lord would convert hundreds by calling to one who had rebelled against Him.

16 *Aminadab*
An Unlikely Missionary

Helaman 5

Alma, Amulek, and Zeezoram preach to the Zoramites

Wicked Zoramites join Lamanites

Tubaloth becomes king of the Lamanites

Coriantumr leads Lamanites to attack the Nephites

Lamanites conquer most Nephite lands

Nephites regain some lands

Nephi and Lehi convert their enemies, including Aminadab

70 BC   60 BC   50 BC   40 BC   30 BC

Aminadab

Nephites and Lamanites

Mulekites

Jaredites

2200 BC 2000 BC   1500 BC   1000 BC   500 BC   AD 1   **AD 421**

An inky mist swirled around Aminadab as he struggled desperately to see.

Do not procrastinate the day of your repentance . . .

He waved a hand as if to drive the fog away, and as the mist cleared slightly, he caught a glimpse of a man—Amulek—standing before a crowd of people, preaching.

For then will come a night of darkness . . .

He was looking at the land of Antionum as it had been many years ago.[1] He could see himself, a young man in the hostile crowd.

Have faith unto repentance . . . and he will encircle you in the arms of his safety.

"Be gone, fools!" Aminadab heard his younger self say, startled by the rancor in his voice.

Amulek had shifted his gaze toward him. His eyes had been filled with compassion.

Exercise your faith unto repentance—cry unto Christ for mercy; for he is mighty to save . . .

"You will no longer bind me down to a foolish belief in Christ!" Aminadab had shouted then. Darkness began to swirl around him once more, and the memory of the preacher faded from view. "You will be cast down to hell by the wrath of God!" Aminadab's younger self was still screaming. Fear took hold on him as he was swallowed up in darkness.

Look and live.

The voice, now just a whisper, echoed all around him. Aminadab could not stand or see, and there seemed to be no hope of escaping the blackness. Panic overwhelmed him, and he thrashed about in an attempt to take hold of something—anything.

Just as he felt he would succumb to despair, a hand reached out of the darkness, touching his shoulder. Aminadab screamed and jerked back.

The servant fell backward and covered his face as Aminadab sat upright in bed. His eyes darted wildly about the room, and he was covered with sweat. Struggling to regain his composure, he drew in a steadying breath, suddenly conscious of how he must appear to his servant.

"How dare you wake me! What is the meaning of this?" Aminadab hissed.

The servant knelt meekly, "Forgive me, my lord, but we have received news from the north. Zarahemla has fallen to the Nephites."

The sun was just clearing the eastern mountains when Aminadab strode into the royal court. He spared brief glances of acknowledgment to the regent kings from around the land of Nephi—the Lamanite homeland—and stopped before the grand monarch.

King Tubaloth[2] looked down from his throne at the faithful man in front of him. Aminadab was something of a legend among his people, having served the kingdom since the days of Amalickiah and Ammoron, and Tubaloth had depended on his counsel during his three decades on the Lamanite throne. Though Aminadab's hair was now gray and he moved with a limp—a keepsake from his years of battle—the king had never seen him like this. Aminadab looked . . . tired.

"My lords, we intended to have this war council later today," the king began, addressing the body of men. "But I am told that new developments call for our immediate attention." The king glanced at Aminadab and then continued. "I received word just this morning that Zarahemla is lost." The reaction, as expected, was immediate.

"How can this be?" one man cried out incredulously. "Who is to blame for this?"

"We must strike quickly," said another. "We must overwhelm them before they can refortify their lands."

"The situation is more dire than you realize," Aminadab stated evenly, speaking over the group. Turning to the king, he continued. "This was not a military victory. Our people have become *converted*. They have been convinced of the power of the Nephite God."

Silence followed his words, and it seemed the council did not know how to respond to this bizarre news. Then, one by one, the men began to smile, and some chuckled.

"Be silent, fools!" spat the king. "Do not take this news lightly."

"I have served as a leader among this people for more than forty years," Aminadab said as he stepped forward and moved among the other kings. "I have lived to see the fall of Zerahemnah at the River Sidon, the failed decade-long war waged by Amalickiah and Ammoron, and the monumental disaster of Coriantumr's invasion—but I have *never* seen anything like what has just happened in the north.

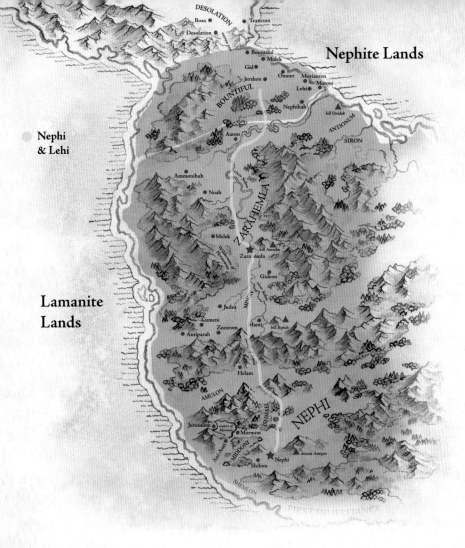

Nephite Lands

Lamanite Lands

Nephi & Lehi

"All of us have celebrated as we've enjoyed victory after victory against the Nephites over the last five years. We have taken and maintained more enemy lands than ever before in the history of our nation. The Nephites have been reduced to but a shadow of their former glory—we even conquered their capital, Zarahemla."

Aminadab stopped pacing. "You may have heard that earlier this year, Nephi renounced his position as chief judge of the Nephites." His statement was met with renewed snickering and derisive comments.

Aminadab leaned behind the nearest man, who was chuckling to himself, and spoke directly in his ear. "Laugh while you can." The man jumped in his seat and quieted quickly. Aminadab glanced at the others humorlessly. "Nephi is more dangerous now than ever. He and his brother, Lehi, have taken it upon themselves to preach. These sons of Helaman walked fearlessly into the midst of our armies occupying the former Nephite capital." Aminadab's eyes narrowed. "As you well know, the men stationed in the land of Zarahemla are all formidable men of war, yet Nephi and Lehi exerted such great power that they have converted many of our brethren who had dissented from the Nephites." The council began to murmur softly among themselves.

Aminadab went on. "*Eight thousand* of the Lamanites who heard the words of these preachers have turned against their traditions to be baptized into the Nephite church."[3]

Now there was silence. Aminadab let the significance of this news sink in before continuing, "My sources tell me that Nephi and Lehi are headed this way. We will be the next to fall if we do not take immediate and decisive action."

The king leaned forward and asked, "What would you propose?"

"The power of their words is their most potent weapon," Aminadab replied without hesitation. "We must stop them from speaking at all costs." His voice shook a little, as if he were trying to subdue a deep fear. His fear—even more than his words—struck dread into the hearts of the king and his council.

"We will place assassins along the path," the king declared with growing urgency. "They will never reach our lands."

Aminadab gazed at the king intently. "Do not think them so easily defeated. Certainly our brethren in Zarahemla tried to slay them, and yet they live." Aminadab began pacing again, lost in his own desperate thoughts. "We must capture them and cast them into prison, where no one will hear their words." A smile crept over his expression, and he relaxed slightly as a plan unfolded in his mind. "We will leave them there, alone in the darkness, for many days with no food. We will break them." He nodded slightly to himself, assured of his plan. "And then we will take them before the people—and slay them."

The king nodded. "How many men shall we send to capture them?"

Aminadab turned again to the king with a grave expression. "An army, Lord Tubaloth. It must be a whole army.[4] And your men *must* be instructed to bind them and gag them. Whatever the cost, they must not let their prisoners speak. Men like this have great power."

"How do you understand so much concerning this?" one of the council asked respectfully.

Aminadab turned an ominous gaze on the man. "I used to belong to their church. I used to be one of them."

Once instructions and orders had been given, the council cleared. King Tubaloth lifted a flask of wine and turned a curious eye on Aminadab.

"You once belonged to the Nephite church?" Tubaloth smiled as if he could scarcely believe it. "You?"

Aminadab sat next to the king's throne and sighed heavily. "I was raised in that cursed church. It wasn't until I was a young man that I began to learn the truth."

Tubaloth looked on questioningly, offering Aminadab some wine and encouraging him to continue, but Aminadab sat silent a moment longer, lost in his reverie. At last he swallowed deeply from the king's flask. He returned the bottle and continued.

"A man named Zoram led a group of Nephites who separated themselves in the land of Antionum. When I first heard his teachings, I knew that I could be freed from the tyranny of the law of Moses taught by the Nephite orthodoxy. Zoram taught us that there would be no Christ, and thus there was no point to all the ridiculous practices associated with His worship. Those who understood that truth were a chosen people and would receive a great reward in the next life. I became wealthy by heeding his teachings. Life among the Zoramites was easy. I could live the way that I wished." He took back the king's flask and emptied it.

Aminadab paused, and his expression darkened. "Then the missionaries came. Alma, Amulek, Zeezrom, and others invaded our peace and arrogantly proclaimed their God and the future coming of Christ." He sneered. "The only success they had was with the poor. We would not bow to the childishness of their traditions—the belief in a Christ that should come. No man knows what is to come."

Still lost in his thoughts, Aminadab repeated the words again, as if trying to convince himself. "No man knows what is to come."

The plans fell into place exactly as Aminadab had commanded. The army was assembled, and as Nephi and Lehi entered the land of Nephi, they were taken and cast into prison. There they were left without food for many days.

"Now is the time," Aminadab advised as he approached the king. Tubaloth looked up from where he stood surveying the assembly that was preparing to enter the prison.

"We have defeated them!" the king announced jubilantly to the group. "Now let us finish this and take them to be slain!"

The building was ancient, having been built more than one hundred years ago in the days of King Noah.[5] Although cells lined the walls, the Nephite prisoners were chained in the midst of an open arcade. The company of executioners entered the dungeon and gathered around Nephi and his brother. Aminadab, who had been so filled with apprehension about confronting them, now scoffed. The two men looked pitiful. Weary and starved, they lacked the strength even to rise. Pathetic.

When Nephi and Lehi lifted their gaze, Aminadab reached out to take hold of them. Yet when he looked into the men's eyes, his hands began to shake slightly. Hopelessness—it wasn't there. Aminadab had expected to see men who were broken, defeated. Yet their eyes shone, as if lit by some internal torch.

Aminadab lurched backward as if to protect himself from wild beasts. As he did so, Nephi and Lehi seemed to burst into flame.

The crowd gasped in horrified amazement as flames encircled the two men. Aminadab's face drained of color, and his mouth opened in a silent cry as the Nephites stood. Nephi and Lehi looked around the room, their expressions puzzled yet serene. A certain majesty fell over them as they stood. Nephi moved his hand through the flames and then turned, smiling to his brother. Aminadab's mouth gaped open as he stared at the mist of light that flared brightly but did not consume the Nephites. In fact, they appeared to be strengthened by it.

Lehi turned to the dumbstruck crowd and smiled. "Fear not," he said gently.

"For behold, it is God that has shown unto you this marvelous thing," Nephi added.

The soft-spoken words pierced Aminadab like a knife, ringing both ominous and frightening in his ears. As he glanced around, it was clear that the other men felt the same. When Amniadab looked back at the prisoners, Nephi was staring directly at him.

"Ye cannot slay us." The earth shook beneath their feet and the walls of the prison trembled.

Aminadab closed his eyes, then covered his ears and cried, "Their words! Don't listen to their words! Run!"

He succeeded only in stumbling a few steps before darkness enclosed him. *No*, he thought frantically as his eyes darted about. Memories of his dreams came flooding back, and a solemn fear gripped his heart.

At that moment, a voice pierced the thick gloom. From somewhere above him, he heard it, powerful and piercing yet perfectly mild, as if it were a whisper. The words only increased his terror.

Repent ye, repent ye, and seek no more to destroy my servants whom I have sent unto you to declare good tidings.

The intensity of the voice was overwhelming, and the earth shook again at the sound of it. Aminadab was certain that the prison walls would not withstand the quaking of the ground, but, miraculously, the walls held. Again the voice returned with the same terrible intensity as before.

Repent ye, repent ye, for the kingdom of heaven is at hand; and seek no more to destroy my servants.

A third time the ground shook, and Aminadab crumbled under the weight of his fear. He wept like a terrified child, covering his face in the darkness. The voice came once more, and he was certain the earth would open up and swallow him into a vast abyss.

Aminadab willed his eyes to focus in the inky blackness, desperate to escape the voice. Then he saw it. An opening in the cloud of darkness. He could see Nephi and Lehi, their faces shining like angels. They inclined themselves toward the voice, lifting their eyes and smiling as if speaking to the source of it.

Look and live.

Aminadab recognized the words of the missionaries from so long ago. Without taking his eyes off of Nephi and Lehi, he called out to the people around him, quietly at first, and then crying aloud like a man who had discovered water in a desert.

"Turn and look! All of you look . . . look and live." Slowly the moans of agony and fear on all sides subsided as his words subdued the bonds of their terror. The darkness surrounding the men began to break slightly, allowing the light reach their eyes. For a long while they simply stared at the warm glow emanating from the faces of Nephi and Lehi. The peace it offered sustained them while they gazed upon the servants of God, yet they were still painfully aware of the darkness that held them captive.

Somewhere in the void, one of the Lamanites called to Aminadab. It was the voice of a man, yet the words were spoken with the humility of a child.

"What do all these things mean, and with whom do these men converse?"

"They do converse with the angels of God," he answered

Another voice reached out to him, pleading, "What shall we do, that this cloud of darkness may be removed from overshadowing us?"

The words he had heard long ago in the land of Antionum came back to him, and Aminadab spoke them with conviction. "You must repent, and cry unto the voice, even until ye shall have faith in Christ, who was taught unto you by Alma, and Amulek, and Zeezrom."

Exercise your faith unto repentance—cry unto Christ for mercy; for he is mighty to save …

He had once mocked these words, but now he clung to them as a most precious gift, a lifeline to save him when nothing else could. He found to his joy and surprise that much strength came in offering this simple testimony, which grew as he spoke. He lifted his voice and called to those around him one more. "And when ye shall do this, the cloud of darkness shall be removed from overshadowing you." As the words left his mouth, he collapsed to the earth and cried out to the Lord as he had not done since his youth. He felt the weight of his rebellion against God and of a life dedicated to the vain and selfish things of the world. Memories of those he had led away from the Church of God and of the Lamanites whose hearts he had hardened against the truth filled his thoughts. As his life of sin harrowed up his soul and the darkness closed in around his heart, he poured out his soul to Christ, pleading for mercy and forgiveness from the God he had forsaken. As he did so, his heart was slowly filled with a resplendent light that eradicated the darkness that bound him. He had a new heart and a new soul.

When he finally stood once more and looked about him, the cloud of darkness was indeed gone, and a glorious light shone forth. The pillar of fire no longer encircled only the prophets. It fell over all those who were in the prison, bathing them in a holy luminance.

He will encircle you in the arms of his safety.

He remembered Amulek's words, and the joy in his heart was far too powerful to express with words. All around him, each man emanated a light that was too great to be contained. The prison glowed in an otherworldly radiance, and an overwhelming glory surrounded them all with a warmth and power that seemed to almost consume their flesh. Yet no man would turn away for the joy that they felt.

Some of the men began to speak, and their words were both marvelous and powerful, so much so that they could not be written or even heard with mortal ears. They were understood through the Spirit. Nephi and Lehi stood in the center of it all, their faces radiant with joy.

Peace.

The voice returned, yet this time Aminadab felt no fear. It sounded different to him somehow—pleasant, quiet, and kind, yet just as powerful.

Peace be unto you, because of your faith in my Well Beloved, who was from the foundation of the world.

"And what happened after the voice spoke?" a Lamanite woman asked.

Aminadab looked at the multitude gathered in the village square to hear his preaching. He smiled at the families sitting close to one another, listening carefully to every word, but as he opened his mouth to speak, no words would come out. Looking up to heaven and remembering that day, the tears flowed, and he was helpless to stop them. The Spirit of the Lord surrounded his listeners, just as the pillar of fire had encircled him in the prison only days before.

He finally drew his gaze back to the multitude. The people were shedding tears of their own, unsure why their hearts felt so full.

"We saw the heavens open," Aminadab said, his voice filled with emotion. "And angels came down and ministered unto us. They told us that we should marvel not, neither should we doubt, but that we should declare the message of Christ throughout all the regions round about."

"We know that you have spoken truth." One of the village elders stood and addressed his people. "Did not our hearts burn within us as he spoke? Could we not feel the power of his witness?" The people nodded, their eyes still brimming with tears. Turning to Aminadab, he raised the question that all his people were thinking. "Now what shall we do?"

Look and live, Aminadab thought. He gave thanks to God that he had been snatched from the edge of the abyss and brought into His glorious light. God had employed him—the most unlikely of missionaries, a rebel against the light of heaven—to help his brethren find light in the darkness. They would, in turn, become an unfaltering witness, testifying among the people of what they had seen and heard.

Because of the missionary efforts of the three hundred souls who had witnessed the marvelous event in the prison that day, the greater part of the Lamanites were converted and became a righteous people. The firmness and steadfastness of their faith exceeded even that of the Nephites.

The conquered lands of the Nephites were returned to their rightful owners without further violence, and peace was established in all the land. The Lamanites did return to Zarahemla, this time as preachers and missionaries. There they would teach with great power and authority and do much to bring the Nephites to join them as humble followers of God and of the Christ that would come.

In the years to come, the Lamanites would continue to be stalwart examples of faith in Christ. Even as the Nephite nation fell into sin, God raised up Samuel, a Lamanite, to testify of the coming of Christ. In five short years from his prophesy, the long-awaited sign was given that Jesus, the Savior of the world, was born.

But a plague of evil quickly infested the land. A scourge of robbers and secret combinations would take hold among the Nephites and, eventually, the new generation of Lamanites as well. No power on earth could stop them—until the chief judge, Lachoneus, was inspired to do something never before heard of in the history of the children of Lehi—but that's another story.

Endnotes

1   The only clue we have to Aminadab's past is his reference to the teachings of Christ that he had received from missionaries Alma, Amulek, and Zeezrom (Helaman 5:41). The only mission mentioned in the Book of Mormon that all three of these men participated in was a mission to the Zoramites in Alma 31–34. Aminadab could also have been referencing another missionary journey that we don't have record of, but for the sake of this story, I am sticking with what we have in the record.

    Matthew Roper wrote a brief but excellent exploration of parallel themes found in the preachings of Alma, Amulek, and Zeezrom as well as in the events with Nephi and Lehi in the prison, which inspired my approach to this story ("Was Aminadab a Zoramite?" *Insights* 24:1, 2004). You can read this article at www.mi.byu.edu.

2   It is unclear who the Lamanite king was at this time, but it is feasible that Tubaloth, son of Ammoron, is still king, seeing as he is last mentioned in Helaman 1:16.

3   I think it's easy to forget how incredible Nephi and Lehi's missionary journey to retake the captured lands of the Nephites really was. There was no military recourse left to the people to retake their lands (Helaman 4:18–19), and so Nephi and his brother devoted themselves entirely to the ministry, first preaching to the Nephites but then marching straight into enemy territory to convert the Lamanites, which they certainly did. Another important thing to remember is that they not only converted Lamanites, but they also did what had never been done by even the greatest of missionaries—they converted Nephite dissenters. This was unprecedented even on a small scale.

4   I think the fear of those in the land of Nephi was real and palpable. I find it incredible that they would send an entire army to take just two men (Helaman 5:21).

5   Helaman 5:21 tells us that Nephi and Lehi were thrown into the same prison Ammon was cast into in the days of Limhi. This gives us a specific location (the city of Nephi) and an idea of just how old this prison structure was. Limhi's father, Noah, initiated many construction projects in his day, building a grand palace, towers, and many spacious buildings (Mosiah 11:8–13). It seems very likely, considering his temperament, that he was also the one who built the prison.

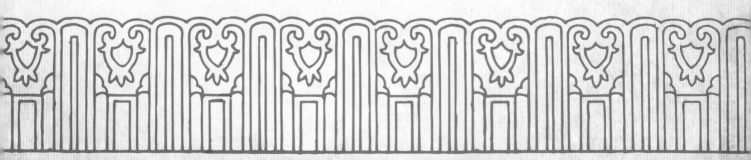

To defeat an invincible army of Gadianton robbers, one leader would be inspired with a plan never before attempted in the history of the Nephites.

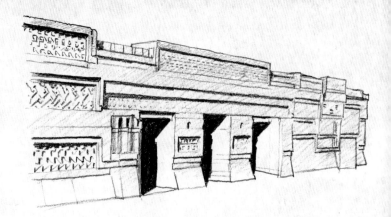

17 Lachoneus
Bane of the Gadiantons

≫ 3 Nephi 1–6 ≪

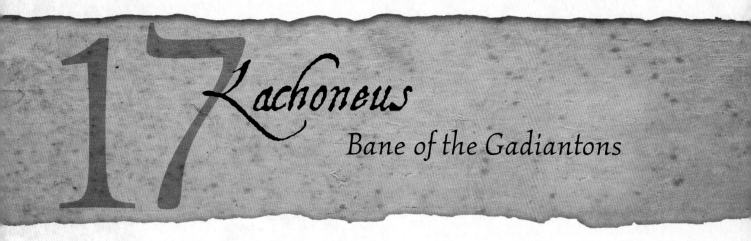

Lachoneus is chief judge
The sign of Christ's birth

Gadianton robbers increase in power

Great wars and contentions
Robbers are driven back
Robbers attack again
Giddianhi's epistle
Lachoneus gathers his people
Robbers "sally forth" but find no food
Giddianhi killed in battle
Robbers lay seige but are destroyed
Zemnarihah hung

AD 1   AD 10   AD 13 AD 14 AD 15 AD 16 AD 17 AD 18 AD 19 AD 20 AD 21

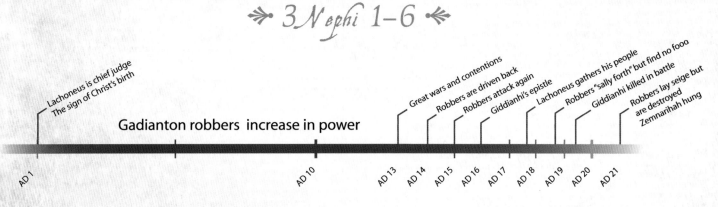

Lachoneus

Nephites and Lamanites
Mulekites

Jaredites

2200 BC 2000 BC   1500 BC   1000 BC   500 BC   AD 1   AD 421

"The wolves have come down from the mountains," a peasant boy whispered to his sister. He was peering around the back wall of the hovel that had once been their home. Urgently taking the girl's arm, he prepared to lead her away, but she was reluctant to leave the only home she had ever known. Pleading but resolute, he looked into his sister's eyes. "We can't escape from them. We will be safe only behind the walls of Zarahemla. We cannot wait any longer. Come quickly now, before they see us."

At this final urging, the girl allowed herself to be led, and the two children disappeared into the trees. Behind them they left a community, once thriving with robust fields and vigorous flocks, now barren and empty—a desolate wasteland.

Beyond the lonely homes, vacant farms, and destitute pastures, the shadowy figures of men could be seen. Hanging from their bodies was a combination of exotic treasures and the basest coverings the wilderness could provide. Their heads were shaved but covered with a plated headgear. Their skin was dyed in blood. They wore only the skin of a lamb about their loins, yet alongside their ghastly coverings, fine jade, obsidian, and gold adorned their arms, legs, and necks—the blood prizes of their terrible vocation.

Their leader and chief walked before them. Arrayed in the trappings of a dark king, Giddianhi entered the lands of the Nephites with an air of entitlement. As he surveyed the cities they passed through, however, his step began to falter and a haunting realization began to form in his mind. City after city was abandoned, bereft of life and crops. As the motley gang continued to travel, looking for grains to strip from the fields and supplies to pillage, Giddianhi began to feel a pang of hunger.

"Lachoneus, you devil," Giddianhi hissed to himself. "Where is all the *food!*"

The sun was high over the city of Zarahemla[1] when the chief judge and governor of the land, Lachoneus, walked the top of the perimeter wall with his entourage. Concerned for the safety of his people, he turned to one of his counselors.

"What have you heard from the local leaders? Have all of our villagers arrived to the fortified lands?"

"Tens of thousands of refugees have arrived," the man began. "We believe that the vast majority is here. Small groups still straggle in from time to time."

Lachoneus considered this news for a moment and then asked, "And the proclamation that we made throughout the land? Are the people still bringing their flocks and yield? Have they destroyed what remains?"

"The people have been obedient to all your words," the man answered confidently.

Turning now to a man of powerful stature on his right, Lachoneus asked with a sense of foreboding, "Captain, what report do you have from the outskirts of the land?"

Gidgiddoni was the chiefest of the chief captains of the Nephites—a man of great skill as a soldier but also a mighty prophet of God. "The robbers are coming," he began. "My lord knows that Giddianhi and his armies have begun to leave their mountain strongholds. They have invaded some of the outer lands. We received word just this morning from two orphans that the robbers have advanced as far as Gideon and are preparing to cross the Sidon. They are almost upon us."

Lachoneus's countenance changed immediately to a look of concern, "Orphans? Have arrangements been made? Are they being cared for?"

The chief captain smiled at the irony. Even at this time of national emergency, a time when the very sword of destruction threatened their existence, their beloved chief judge's first concern was the welfare of two young orphans who had found their way to his protection.

"Yes, my lord," Gidgiddoni assured. "My wife and her sisters are seeing to their needs."

Comforted, Lachoneus turned to survey the activities within the walls. "We've had so many orphans and widows in the last few years," he said quietly. As the governor looked upon the scene before him, his eyes lighted on the vast stores of supplies gathered by his people. "Do we have enough to last out this siege—with all these people?"

"Have no fear, dear Lachoneus," replied his captain assertively, placing a comforting hand on the governor's shoulder. "The Lord has blessed us greatly, and we have more than enough. We have supplies to feed our people for seven years."

"I'm starving!" Giddianhi sat in a dark lodge with his commanders. Each man looked more piqued than they ever had in their lives. "We need to find food!"

Zemnarihah, Giddianhi's second in command, leaned forward. "Perhaps we could plant crops— revitalize the abandoned fields."

"Don't be a fool," Giddianhi sneered, dismissing the idea out of hand. "Would you have us spread our forces across the land? That would only leave us vulnerable to the attacks of the cursed Nephites."

"Not so," Zemnarihah pressed on. "We are strong, and we may station our forces where we will. The gutless Nephites will not come out of their fortifications."

"No." Giddianhi's eyes flickered upon each man. "There is no more time. We must attack now or all is lost.

The men murmured their approval. Giddianhi, slowly rising, continued. "For months we have been living on whatever we can find in the wilderness, carefully restricting our food, not knowing where our next meal may come from. No more! Zemnarihah, break out the rations. Give every man all he can eat!" The commanders began to rise, cheering as they did so.

"And on the morrow," continued Giddianhi. "Tell your men to array themselves for war. By our might we shall no longer go hungry, for we shall feast on the stores of our enemies. Tomorrow the Nephites will fall before us!"

The morning of the battle, Giddianhi and his robber horde approached the Nephites as if from a dark and twisted nightmare. Gruesome headplates adorned their shaved scalps, loose armor[2] hung from their haggard frames, and lambskins were wrapped about their loins—all of it stained with blood.

Giddianhi strode to the front of his ghastly band of robbers and looked across the field to the Nephite army. He could barely contain his delight as he cracked a wicked smile. "They've fallen to the earth!" he shouted back to his men with a laugh. "The Nephites have fallen with fear because of the terror of our army! Cowards and dogs!"

A cry rose up from the robbers that would challenge the courage of even the bravest warrior. Giddianhi strode forward as if to advance on the quivering Nephites, but he stopped abruptly when an arrow slammed into his shield.[3] It took him a moment to absorb the surprise, and then he noticed an epistle attached to the arrow. It was written in his own handwriting:

"Lachoneus, most noble and chief governor of the land, behold, I write this epistle unto you, and do give unto you exceedingly great praise because of your firmness, and also the firmness of your people, in maintaining that which ye suppose to be your right and liberty; yea, ye do stand well, as if ye were supported by the hand of a god . . ."

Giddianhi had written this epistle three years ago in hopes of intimidating Lachoneus into giving up the lands of the Nephites without a fight. The Nephite governor had never answered it. Now Giddianhi's own words began to haunt him as he looked again at his enemies. They were rising to their feet, and he knew now that they had not fallen with fear—they had been praying to their God.

Giddianhi cursed, now consumed with desperation and rage. There was no turning back now. They must conquer or perish.

Another cry rose up from the robbers, and they rushed forward to war. But as they approached the waiting defenders, an unnerving thought pulsed in Giddianhi's mind.

As if ye were supported by the hand of a god . . .

And just as Giddianhi was about to engage the Nephites, he saw it. The Nephites were prepared to meet them as if with the strength of God, for there was no fear in their eyes.

The records of that great and terrible battle describe a slaughter unlike any among all the children of Lehi since he'd arrived in the promised land over six hundred years before. The Nephites truly received their enemies in the strength of the Lord and drove them back to flee into the wilderness. Giddianhi was numbered among the slain.

Two years passed before the robbers reassembled and came against the Nephites again. This time Zemnarihah led the robbers, but they did not attack. The new leader positioned his men to lay siege again to the land and cut off any access to outside resources.

Lachoneus and Captain Gidgiddoni lifted their bowed heads as the prayer was finished and looked over the food laid out before them. The other counselors seated with them waited for Lachoneus to begin before they did the same.

"Please begin without me," the chief judge urged, but no man moved. "Captain, what is our status?"

"I am not sure how long Zemnarihah thinks he can survive," Gidgiddoni began. "His supplies are limited to the hunting parties he sends out to find game, some of which never return to their camps. We have been sending our armies out at night and during the day to engage the robbers, which Zemnarihah has so kindly spread out across the land. Tens of thousands have been destroyed. I think the time of a complete surrender is soon at hand."

"And, Chief Lachoneus," one of his counselors added, "God has blessed and supported us, for we have barely used up half of our stores of food."

Lachoneus sat thoughtfully for a moment. "I, like many of you, was alive to see the marvelous sign of the Savior's birth twenty-one years ago. We were shown such miraculous signs and wonders in the years that followed, but we became complacent. We were no longer impressed by a sign from heaven, and we became hard in our hearts and blind in our minds. We began to disbelieve even that which we had seen and heard."

The governor seemed weighted down by a heavy burden, and he sighed before he could continue. "So many of the children in the rising generation have grown up thinking only of themselves, and they have been led away to join this band of wicked robbers. I want to celebrate our victory over those who would be our enemies, but so many of them should have been our friends and kin." Lachoneus was unashamed at the tear that moistened his cheek as he finished his admonishment. "Pray with me. Pray that God will not only end this war with the robbers, which has plagued us for eight years now, but also that we may have the opportunity to preach the word of God to them—that we may help them to be our brethren again and rejoice with them in those things that will surely come to pass."

Just then a young soldier marched into the room and stood at the entrance. Captain Gidgiddoni rose and met with him briefly and then returned to report. "Zemnarihah is on the move. It seems the robbers have abandoned their designs upon us but instead of surrendering, Zemnarihah has convinced them to march with him into the farthermost parts of the land northward." The captain looked over the council to be sure each man understood the urgency of this news. "Brethren, they are making for the narrow pass."

The severity of this news did not need to be further explained. Many of the enemies of the Nephites had tried[4] to take the narrow pass that led into the land northward, a strategic point that would allow an enemy to entrench themselves on the northern border of the Nephites. Up until this time no enemy had ever succeeded—and Gidgiddoni was not about to let them.

The night before the robbers were to depart, the Nephite captain sent part of his army north along the path of the robbers' retreat. The next day, when the robbers began their march, a Nephite army awaited them. Gidgiddoni had also sent an army to follow them in the south, so as the robbers turned to flee, they found themselves surrounded.

Many thousands surrendered immediately and were taken prisoner. Those hardhearted men who wished to fight to the death were given their wish. They were dispatched by the men of Gidgiddoni— all except Zemnarihah. His execution would be much more public.

The quiet evening was disturbed only by the rhythmic sound of axes striking the trunk of a tree. The sun, low over the western mountains, illuminated the form of a man swaying from its highest branches. Zemnarihah's dreams of conquest and glory had been halted at the end of a rope. Now the tree began to creak and sway. The woodcutters moved back as the trunk cracked and buckled and the tree crashed to the earth.

It was finally over. The only robbers left in the land were in prison. The Nephites, at last, were free!

Lachoneus stood forth and broke the astonished silence by placing all present under covenant:

"May the Lord preserve his people in righteousness and in holiness of heart, that they may cause to be felled to the earth all who shall seek to slay them because of power and secret combinations, even as this man hath been felled to the earth."

The people cried out in response, "May the God of Abraham, and the God of Isaac, and the God of Jacob, protect this people in righteousness, so long as they shall call on the name of their God for protection."

The people broke forth in praise and song, for they were truly delivered from the hands of their enemies.

Hosanna to the Most High God!

Blessed be the name of the Lord God Almighty, the Most High God!

Their hearts were so swollen with joy and thanksgiving that their eyes could not remain dry.[5] Lachoneus watched his people shed tears of gratitude to God. He knew that God had finally delivered them because of their repentance and humility, and not only from their mortal enemies, but also from an everlasting destruction. Lachoneus could see that his people knew it too. Not one among them doubted the words of the holy prophets in the least. They all knew that their prophecies would be fulfilled. Perhaps it was that more than anything that caused his own tears to flow—and he did not restrain them.

The sounds of the prisoners hushed a little when Lachoneus, the prophet Nephi, who was the son of Nephi, and others arrived again at the prison. The cells were crowded, and many of the imprisoned robbers slunk to the back wall when the Nephites drew near. They turned their backs and refused to listen. Many others[6], however, watched with rapt attention as the scriptures were opened to them and as the words of the holy prophets, sweet in the hearts of their newly growing testimonies, were fed to them. These words would change their lives, as they do for all who heed them.

Scarcely more than a decade would pass before all the prophesies were fulfilled concerning the coming of Christ and His appearance in majesty among the children of Lehi. Peace would reign for more than a hundred and fifty years before the curse of secret combinations would again fester in the land. This time, however, it would spell the beginning of the end for the Nephite nation—but that's another story.

Endnotes

1 It's a bit hard to know exactly which lands were fortified from the description in 3 Nephi 3:23:

> And the land which was appointed was the land of Zarahemla, and the land which was between the land Zarahemla and the land Bountiful, yea, to the line which was between the land Bountiful and the land Desolation.

The land of Zarahemla covers a large piece of the Nephites' land southward, and Bountiful borders the narrow neck, which leads to the land of Desolation in the land northward. It seems to say that Lachoneus fortified Zarahemla and all the lands in between up to Bountiful, which just about covers most of the land southward. It's unclear whether he fortified that entire region or just the city centers of those lands, where he could then pull in the villages and farming communities, but it seems to me that the latter is more likely.

2 Even though the robbers' ghastly apparel is described in 3 Nephi 4:7, it does not initially list armor. We are specifically told about the lambskin about their loins, their headplates, and their being dyed with blood. It is not until the end of the verse that it mentions that the terror of their appearance was, in part, due to their armor. Whatever armor they were wearing, I assume it was as horrific as the rest of their garb.

3 I've taken quite a bit of liberty here, but I really wanted a way to introduce Giddianhi's most remarkable and patronizing epistle to Lachoneus. Nothing in the account says that Giddianhi even has a shield much less that he had his epistle shot to him with an arrow.

4 Enemies such as Morianton (Alma 50:32–35), Amalickiah (Alma 51:23–27), Ammoron (Alma 52:9), and perhaps Coriantumr (who made a straight line right through the heart of Nephite lands (Helaman 1), all tried to take the narrow pass.

5 Tears are rarely mentioned in the Book of Mormon, but none of those rare instances has a more dramatic description than what we find for these people in 3 Nephi 4:33: "And their hearts were swollen with joy, unto the gushing out of many tears . . ." They didn't "shed tears" (Ether 6:12) or even "shed many tears" (Mosiah 25:9). They gushed out many tears. This was no small expression of gratitude to their God. The sad news is that in less than ten years from that time, the Nephites would turn against the very God who delivered them (3 Nephi 6:14).

6 It appears that many of the robbers were Lamanites (3 Nephi 1:29). Those robbers who listened to the word of the Lord and who repented and entered into a covenant were released from prison (3 Nephi 5:4). Those who wished to remain identified as Lamanites were given lands of their own according to their numbers (3 Nephi 6:3). I wonder if it was these same Lamanites who were referred to some few years later when "the church was broken up in all the land save it were among a few of the Lamanites who were converted unto the true faith; and they would not depart from it, for they were firm, and steadfast, and immovable, willing with all diligence to keep the commandments of the Lord" (3 Nephi 6:14).

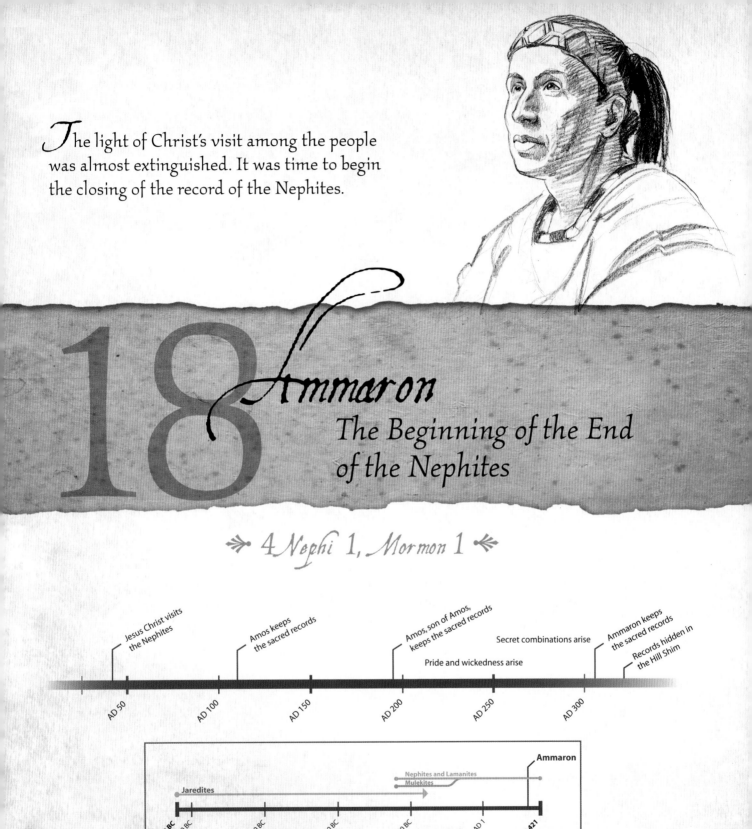

The light of Christ's visit among the people was almost extinguished. It was time to begin the closing of the record of the Nephites.

18 *Ammaron*
The Beginning of the End of the Nephites

❧ *4 Nephi 1, Mormon 1* ❧

Jesus Christ visits the Nephites

Amos keeps the sacred records

Amos, son of Amos, keeps the sacred records

Secret combinations arise

Pride and wickedness arise

Ammaron keeps the sacred records

Records hidden in the Hill Shim

AD 50   AD 100   AD 150   AD 200   AD 250   AD 300

Ammaron

Nephites and Lamanites
Mulekites

Jaredites

2200 BC   2000 BC   1500 BC   1000 BC   500 BC   AD 1   AD 421

In the land northward in AD 319, the rain outside came down in torrents, and dark clouds obscured the sun. Ammaron watched the downpour for a few moments before standing to light a lamp. The flickering flame brightened the room, illuminating the work that lay before him.

As he sat down once more, Ammaron looked over the words he had penned so far and sighed. For nine generations his family had kept the sacred records of the Nephite nation. They had been handed down from father to son[1] over the past four hundred and eleven years, each new guardian of the precious work pledging to protect and preserve it.[2]

But Ammaron was the last.[3]

He dipped his brush into the ink and began to write once more.[4] After only a few minutes, however, his gaze wandered toward the plates stacked within reach. Although his purpose was to make an account of his days, he often found himself drawn to the writings of his ancestors. Ammaron put down his brush and reached for the plates containing the writings of his great-grandfather, Nephi, the son of Nephi.

"Master?"

Ammaron turned toward the voice and saw a boy of eight years standing in the doorway, hoping to be admitted. Ammaron smiled and held out a weathered hand in greeting. "You may enter."

The boy stepped carefully around the records on the floor and stopped by Ammaron's side. The wizened record keeper had seen this boy at his lessons and remembered him as an attentive student.[5] Now the child looked down at the heavy paper before Ammaron and asked, "What are you writing?"

"Not much yet. I am recording the doings of our people." His expression clouded over. "It is not a work that lifts my spirits—not like reading the history of years long past," he added wistfully.

"Will you tell me again of those days?" the boy implored.

Ammaron studied the boy's hopeful expression, surprised that one so young would remember—much less take an interest in—the stories he had taught.

"Are you sure you wouldn't rather be outside playing?" The boy gave Ammaron an incredulous look and then pointed to the window, reminding him of the foul weather. Just then squeals of laughter and the chatter of excited young voices could be heard outside the window as children ran through the rain and splashed in the puddles, but the eager young student remained unmoved.

"Please," said the boy. "Tell me again about Jesus."

Ammaron nodded, touched by the boy's plea. He told his young listener about the coming of the Lord Jesus Christ to the land of the Nephites, starting with His resurrection in the old world. Not long after, Christ had descended from heaven and appeared at the temple in the land of Bountiful. Ammaron recounted how Christ had healed the sick, blessed the children, and taught the people His gospel. The Savior of the world had stayed for three days, and he'd changed the lives of the people for generations.

Ammaron looked up to see the boy sitting quietly, listening to every word. He continued. "It has been more than two hundred eighty years since the coming of the Lord Jesus Christ. His teachings and miracles had such a powerful effect on the hearts of the people that for more than one hundred fifty years after his visit[6] there was continual peace in the land, and the Lord blessed the people in all they did." Sadness filled Ammaron's eyes. "But pride began to enter into the hearts of the people. They broke into tribes, divided themselves by class and began to build up churches unto themselves. By the time two hundred forty-four years had passed away, those that chose wickedness far outnumbered the righteous. Then the secret oaths and combinations of Gadianton began to be seen in the land . . ."

Ammaron paused and looked down at his record. "You know the rest. The charge to preserve these sacred records was given to me by my brother thirteen years ago, and what have I had to write? That the whole face of the land is filled with great pride and vanity? Or that a corrupt nature is found among both the Lamanites and the Nephites? Or that the beloved disciples of Jesus who should tarry are rarely seen because of the wickedness of our people?"[7]

Ammaron let his voice trail off and looked out at the rain still coming down in sheets, lost in his own thoughts. Was there any hope for his people now? Would God again redeem a people who had so willfully rebelled against Him?

He was brought out of his reverie by a soft tap on his knee and a small voice asking, "Disciples who should tarry?"

Ammaron smiled and turned back to his young friend. "Yes, indeed. Have I not mentioned them before?" When the boy shook his head, he said, "While He was here, the Lord Jesus Christ chose twelve disciples to be His special witnesses to all the people. My great-grandfather was one of them. He was chosen by the Savior Himself." The boy's eyes grew wide with amazement, and Ammaron continued. "Three of the twelve desired—and were given—a special gift. They will never taste of death until the will of the Father is fulfilled among the children of men, and Christ comes again in His glory."[8]

Ammaron smiled softly. The boy's eyes couldn't get much bigger. "So they've been alive since the coming of Jesus?" he asked. The boy shook his head in wonder, but then a puzzled look crossed his face. "Where are they now?"

"They are still seen occasionally in the land, but I am certain that very soon the Lord will not permit them to stay among us because of the iniquity our people." Sighing heavily, he added, "With them will vanish the work of miracles and healings, and the land will be truly dark to my eyes."[9]

They sat in silence for a moment, listening to the rain. Then the boy looked up and said tentatively, "I wish I could meet them and touch their hands . . . the hands that touched Jesus, my Savior."

Ammaron's heart lifted slightly, touched by the fervor in the child's voice. After a moment, he replied, "If you remain faithful, my boy, I believe you will meet them one day. In fact, I would not be surprised if you found yourself visited by the Lord Himself."[10]

He took the boy by the hand and looked directly into his eyes. "What is your name, child?"

"Mormon, son of Mormon," the boy replied proudly. "I was named after the land of Mormon where—"

"Alma established the Church of God among the people," Ammaron finished incredulously. "Alma was one of my forefathers. It was his son, Alma, who began the keeping of the sacred records in my family. They have been passed down from generation to generation, of which I am the last."

The boy looked concerned. "What will happen to the sacred records when you are gone?"

"The Lord will speak to me by His Holy Spirit, and whatever He tells me to do, that will I do."

They were both silent for a moment, then Ammaron said thoughtfully, "Mormon . . . I will remember your name." As he glanced back toward the window, he saw that the rain had stopped and a ray of light was breaking through the clouds.

When Mormon answered the quiet rap on his door, his heart rejoiced as he looked into the face of the unexpected visitor standing before him. It had been two years since he had seen Ammaron, and it was rumored that the elderly man had left the land.[11] Ammaron looked strangely older but more at peace than Mormon had ever seen him.

"Are the records safe? Is that where you went? To find a safe hiding place for them?" The questions spilled from Mormon all at once as he looked into his old mentor's face.

"Mormon, sit with me and let me speak," Ammaron said gently. The expression in his eyes quite serious. "It is a matter of the gravest importance." Mormon nodded and sat down at once, anxious for his friend to continue.

Ammaron sat beside him. "The Lord has made known unto me by His Holy Spirit what I should do to preserve the record of our people. I have accomplished that which the Lord required of me, and now the Lord has revealed to me that *thou* shalt also bring to pass a great work regarding these writings." The ten-year-old continued to pay close attention.

"I perceive that thou art a sober child, and art quick to observe," Ammaron continued. "Therefore, when ye are about twenty and four years old I would that ye should remember the things that ye have observed concerning this people; and when ye are of that age, go to the land Antum, unto a hill which shall be called Shim; and there have I deposited unto the Lord all the sacred engravings concerning this people."

Mormon nodded slightly, and Ammaron went on. "There ye shall find the small and large plates of Nephi, the plates of brass, the twenty and four gold plates of Ether, the record of Zeniff, the writings of Lehi, King Benjamin, the missionary sons of Mosiah, the epistles of Moroni and Helaman, the words of our Lord and Master Jesus Christ, and all the other sacred records of the people that I have hidden away. Last of all, I have finished my record of the wickedness of my day, and I have sealed all these things in the darkness of the hill.[12] And behold, ye shall take the plates of Nephi unto yourself, and the remainder shall ye leave in the place where they are; and ye shall engrave on the plates of Nephi all the things that ye have observed concerning this people."[13]

Mormon looked overwhelmed but resolute. "I will," he said simply.

"I know this is wisdom in the Lord, and I leave with you my blessing." Ammaron smiled and put his hand on Mormon's shoulder. "You will bring light out of our darkness." Then he departed.

Ammaron had chosen well, and Mormon was as good as his word. As the boy grew, the Lord continued to prepare him to take responsibility for the sacred writings of his people. Mormon did write the sad tale of his day, but the Lord gave him also a special commission to create his own abridged version of the religious history of his people. This record would come forth in the last days and be a great blessing to all the inhabitants of the earth, bringing countless souls unto Christ. It would be named after him—the Book of Mormon.

Endnotes

1   To be clear, the records were not always passed from father to son. There were two instances of the record being passed to a brother for a period of time (Alma 63:1; 4 Nephi 1:47) and one instance where the records were passed from uncle to nephew (Alma 62:11).

2   The first record keeper in Ammaron's lineage was Alma, the son of Alma, in 92 B.C. (Mosiah 28:20).

3   It is unclear why Ammaron had no one to pass the records to within his family lineage. He may not have had any children or brothers to pass the records to, as was the case with an earlier record keeper named Amaleki (Omni 1:25, 30). If Ammaron did have sons, it is also possible that none of them was worthy.

4   The records we know about in the Book of Mormon were described as books and were written (or engraved) on plates. As an artist, I know the importance of planning important details out in advance before jumping into the final piece. In my mind, it's hard to imagine that all records (epistles, records of people like Zeniff or the sons of Mosiah, etc.) were written on plates. I think the most important events made it onto the plates eventually, even if they were first recorded on another material like leather or paper. It makes sense to me that a record would first be written on paper (or something similar) and then engraved on the plates. Regardless of how they really did it, we do know that there were other types of records besides just plates (Helaman 3:15).

5   No one knows if Ammaron and the young Mormon met much before their only recorded conversation in Mormon 1:2–4. I like the possibility that Ammaron was one of those that helped the young boy to be "learned somewhat after the manner of the learning of [his] people" (Mormon 1:2). It seems to be a rather unique set of skills (language and even metallurgical skill [3 Nephi 5:11]) to have to master, and who but a record keeper would be better qualified to teach him? It could have been Ammaron.

6   A.D. 184 (4 Nephi 1:20).

7   The exact date of the departure of the three disciples of Christ that tarried (3 Nephi 28:4–7) is unclear. Mormon was actually the first to mention that they had been taken out of the land (Mormon 1:13, 16), and it very likely happened during the four years of peace between A.D. 323 and A.D. 326 as described in verses 12–13. The last reference to them before they are "taken away out of the land" is a possible reference in 4 Nephi 1:46 in A.D. 301. For the purposes of the story, I introduced the possibility that the disciples were not seen often in the land as an indication of the wickedness of the people.

8   3 Nephi 28:7.

9   Mormon 1:13.

10 Mormon both meets the Three Nephites and sees the Savior (Mormon 1:15; 8:11).

11 Mormon 1:2. It would have seemed natural for Ammaron to have sent for Mormon, but this verse makes it clear that Ammaron came to Mormon.

12 Since Mormon abridged his own record (Mormon 5:9), I feel safe adding just a bit of the words Ammaron spoke to him.

13 Mormon 1:2–4.